The ISTC Handbook of
Technical Writing and
Publication Techniques

The ISTC Handbook of Technical Writing and Publication Techniques

A Practical Guide for Managers, Engineers, Scientists and Technical Publications Staff

Written and illustrated by members of the
Institute of Scientific and Technical Communicators

ISTC Publication Project Leader
Mike Austin DLC, FISTC

ISTC Co-ordinating Editor
Ralph F. Dodd FISTC, MBIM, MJI, AIAgrE

HEINEMANN: LONDON

William Heinemann Ltd
10 Upper Grosvenor Street, London, W1X 9PA

LONDON MELBOURNE TORONTO
JOHANNESBURG AUCKLAND

© Institute of Scientific and Technical Communicators, 1985
First published, 1985

British Library Cataloguing in Publication Data

The ISTC handbook of technical writing and
    publication techniques: a practical guide for
    managers, engineers, scientists and technical
    publications staff.
    1. Technical writing
    I. Austin, Mike   II. Dodd, Ralph F.
    III. Institute of Scientific and Technical
    Communications
    808'.0666021   T11

    ISBN 0-434-90354-X

Typeset by Rowland Phototypesetting Ltd,
Bury St Edmunds, Suffolk
Printed in England by
St Edmundsbury Press,
Bury St Edmunds, Suffolk

Foreword

In 1948 Sir Ernest Gower, a senior career civil servant, dissatisfied with the language which his colleagues used to communicate with government, with each other and with the public, wrote a book entitled *Plain Words*. His objective was to simplify the expression of civil service thinking whether in writing or speech, by the use of language that yielded ready and un-ambiguous understanding of what was intended by the communicator. The book, revised last in 1977, still enjoys its justified reputation as a reference and guide.

This *ISTC Handbook*, one would hope, will do as much for technical writers as Sir Ernest did for communicators on everyday subjects. The ten chapters and three appendixes of this volume have been written by authors who are professionally qualified to pass on their own experiences, conclusions, and recommendations derived through the conduct of their own professions.

Technical writing is not like writing a letter or a novel which may be read through from beginning to end once and then shelved and forgotten. The *ISTC Handbook*, in over 200 pages, presents guidelines on how to set out clearly, carefully, and conscientiously, information or instruction whether in words or in symbols (including line drawings) with precise understanding of what the words and symbols, phrases and sentences mean. (By comparison I find Roget's *Thesaurus* imprecise in its sup-posedly synonymous definitions.) This precision is essential since tech-nical expression of words and symbols may have profound effects if misread, affecting as it may, health, safety, life or death and at a much lesser but still vital level, the economic and useful benefits to be derived from proper understanding of how to operate, maintain and service a machine of any description.

The *ISTC Handbook* may well have to be used as a constant reference to remind or check whether that which is being communicated technically is sustaining the reader at the highest levels of complete understanding, without any misunderstanding. As the authors point out, it is just as necessary to know what *not* to do as it is to know what to do since what to do is the corrective action for what not to do.

Finally, the printing mysteries of publication are described and ex-plained.

Monty Finniston
January, 1985

P.S. I only hope that this Foreword is written to the exacting standards of clarity demanded by the authors of the *ISTC Handbook*.

The Institute of Scientific and Technical Communicators dedicates this work to the late Tony Taylor, FISTC, whose contributory chapters were uncompleted at his sudden death. The technical authors he taught will remember him with gratitude and affection for opening the way to a profession of growing international importance.

Contents

Acknowledgments

In addition to the authors and co-ordinating editor listed below, I would like to thank our most capable typists, Susan Bradley and Dorothy Wakeford, and the following members of the ISTC Book Committee who assisted in the planning and administration of the book: Andrew Charlesworth, Student; Brian Neylan, MISTC; and Philip Thompson, AMISTC

I would also like to gratefully acknowledge the valuable assistance provided by the following:

Brian Edwards of the UK Civil Aviation Authority who pioneered and those other colleagues of Mr Marden who shared the development of the quality control procedures which are reflected in Chapter 8.

APV International Ltd for permission to use a number of their illustrations in Chapter 4.

Mr R. W. H. Wood, MISTC and the Barking College of Technology for permission to use their illustrations in Chapter 4.

Industrial Artists Ltd who designed the ISTC logo.

TEK Translation and International Print Ltd, who through the kind interest of their Mr John Fisher supplied translations for the foreign language captions, and invaluable practical notes for the chapter on translations.

Lonsdale Technical Services Ltd for their close interest in the chapter on translations and general support for the whole project.

M & E White Consultants Ltd for information on ILSAM, the International Language for Servicing and Maintenance.

The Association of Special Libraries and Information Bureaux (ASLIB) for information on their organization and services.

Portsmouth College of Art and Design for permission to use the gearbox illustration in Chapter 4.

Gestetner International Ltd, Gestetner Compugraphic Ltd and Interscan Communications Systems Limited for their assistance in preparing the chapter on technical publications equipment.

Finally, I would like to express gratitude to my own employer, HML (Engineering) Ltd, for the support they have always provided, both for this project and for other professional ISTC activities.

Mike Austin
Chairman of ISTC Book Committee

Contributing Authors

MIKE AUSTIN, DLC, FISTC (a former vice-president of the ISTC) is currently Publications and Publicity Officer of HML (Engineering) Ltd, manufacturers of aircraft hydraulic test equipment. Has worked as a technical author with de Havilland Engine Co., Peabody Ltd (Gas Cleaning Division) and two technical publications agencies. Is author of two books relative to driving instruction and road safety – 'Learning to Drive a Car' (Odhams) and 'Accident Black Spot – a Critical Study of Road Safety Policy and Practice' (Pelican Original) which latter work received high praise from the then Minister of Transport, Mrs Barbara Castle. Has had many articles published on a wide range of technical and lay subjects.

PETE GREENFIELD, MISTC has worked as a Technical Author for Sangamo Weston Ltd, and Gestetner Manufacturing Ltd., and is at present the Senior Technical Author/Training Officer for Gestetner International Ltd. Part-time lecturer in technical writing at City University.

LARRY IRVIN, MISTC, trained as a technical illustrator with the original Fairey Aviation Company where he worked for a total of 19 years in several divisions of the company. In 1962 he joined a technical publications agency where he later became senior illustrator. For the past 15 years he has been a freelance technical illustrator and graphics consultant. He is also an examiner in continuous tone for the City and Guilds of London Institute.

JOHN KIRKMAN, MA, PhD, FISTC, is a consultant on technical communication. Formerly, he was the Director of the Communication Studies Unit at the University of Wales Institute of Science and Technology, Cardiff. Since 1963, he has consulted, advised, and run short courses for more than 200 companies, research centres and government departments in 14 countries. He obtained his degrees in English and a Certificate in Education from the University of Nottingham. He has been a Visiting Lecturer in Technical Communication at the University of Michigan and a Visiting Fellow in Linguistics at Princeton University. Dr. Kirkman has published seven books and more than 60 articles, including *Good Style for Scientific and Engineering Writing* (Pitman 1980) and *Effective Writing* (with Christopher Turk, Spon 1980). He was given the Outstanding Article Award by the Society for Technical Communication (USA) in 1974.

E. J. MARDEN, MISTC, AMRAeS retired in May 1981 from his post as head of the Publications Unit of the Airworthiness Division of the United Kingdom Civil Aviation Authority, and was previously editor of British Civil Airworthiness Requirements with the United Kingdom Air Registration Board. He is a one-time Secretary of the Presentation of Technical Information Discussion Group at University College, London, and a lecturer on the Presentation of Technical Information at the United Kingdom Airworthiness Course.

DENIS TYSON, FISTC, Regional Director – Lonsdale Technical Services Ltd. Mr Tyson trained as an RAF wireless apprentice at Cranwell 1943–45, subsequently serving abroad in Japan, Egypt, and W. Germany. An abiding interest in languages was usefully combined with his technical experience, when for five years he was employed as a specialist linguist and instructor. Since leaving the services, Mr Tyson taught French and Russian at evening classes for 15 years, whilst working as a Technical Author and Publications Manager. Since 1968 he has acted as examiner for the City and Guilds Institute in Technical Communication Techniques; he is a founding member of the ISTC and serves on the standing committee for Education and Training. In his present post, and for the past 25 years, he has been professionally engaged in providing Technical Publications services to industrial organizations, and other establishments.

JOHN WAKEFORD, FISTC has since 1977 been a freelance technical writing consultant. For 17 years previously he was employed by Technical Designs Ltd (now Lonsdale Technical Services Ltd) as a project author involved in multi-volume handbooks for large systems, and was an installation engineer/technical author with Air Trainers Ltd, for five years before that. As a regular in the RAF he gained an engineering training and also served as a technical instructor.

ISTC CO-ORDINATING EDITOR

RALPH F. DODD, FISTC, MBIM, MJI, AIAgrE is deputy editor of the monthly magazine *Chartered Mechanical Engineer* published by the Institution of Mechanical Engineers, and was previously assistant editor of the same publisher's bi-monthly magazines *Automotive Engineer* and *Railway Engineer*. Prior to 1977 he had varied experience in technical journalism and publishing including 2½ years as a sales promotion manager with British Steel and a shorter period as technical editor with Production Engineering Research Association. From 1960–68 he was technical author for agricultural machinery manufacturer Howard Rotavator, responsible for complete publications production including writing, designing and print buying for a wide variety of handbooks and workshop manuals. Has had numerous articles published on a variety of topics.

Introduction

In an era of continuously expanding technology, clear, concise and accurate communication of technical information and instructions is increasingly becoming of paramount importance; indeed, at times it may be the crucial factor in a life or death situation involving thousands of people.

Even at consumer level, clear instructions can be vital to the success of a product. A study by the management of a leading British discount store revealed that when customer complaints of unsatisfactory products were investigated in depth, frequently the main cause of complaint was the back-up material that the manufacturer did, or did not supply. Many of the complaints fell within four broad categories:

- Instructions too complicated for the user of the product.
- Instructions that lump together a range of models, leaving the purchaser to sort out those applicable.
- Instructions that are downright misleading, such as cabinet assembly instructions that caused most people to assemble the hinges upside down.
- The complete absence of instructions. This caused a lot of problems in the marketing of a non-stick saucepan.

At higher levels of technology, the safety and operational efficiency of highly complicated and enormously expensive equipment, such as a nuclear power station or an airliner, can depend on the quality of the operating and maintenance manuals provided for the personnel using and servicing the equipment.

A survey conducted in the USA by the Air Force Institute, Humanities Department, among prominent successful engineers, showed that the respondents spent 24% of their time writing and 31% working with material written by others. They frequently find fault with the material with which they work and believe that the ability to write clearly is important or crucial when a man is considered for advancement.

In the British armed services and some sections of British manufacturing, notably the aircraft industry, considerable attention has been paid to this subject, and there are many examples of first-class technical communications in the form of manuals, wall charts, brochures and so on.

Certain British universities and colleges of technology provide tuition in technical communication both written and graphic, and this has helped to raise the standard. In particular, the City and Guilds courses for technical authors and illustrators have helped to provide an educational foundation for practitioners in the technical publications field. But in a global context such enlightenment is rare. The high quality of training provided by British art colleges for technical illustrators, for example, is virtually non-existent elsewhere in the world.

Even in Britain, there are still many, both in industry and education, who have no conception of what technical communication is all about. The following true case exemplifies the degree of ignorance that can exist. The specification for some aircraft test equipment included a requirement for an operating and maintenance manual to ATA 101 standard, and firms tendering for the contract to supply this equipment were required to include a separate cost for the manual. One firm submitting a tender gave a manual cost figure equivalent to 0.005% of the total contract price. The firm that was awarded the contract actually spent approximately 5% of the contract price on the manual. The difference between 0.005% and 5% is a quantitative indication of the degree of ignorance of some engineering managements of the scale of documentation required for the efficient use of intricate engineering equipment.

Similar degrees of ignorance also exist in many areas of the educational system, as a result of which many undergraduates experience the utmost difficulty in communicating technical concepts with any reasonable degree of clarity and concision. Abroad, the situation is often just as bad, if not worse. At the University of Toronto students are required to write an acceptable 300 word essay on a general topic before they can register for their third year. In 1982 149 failed to pass.

The Institute of Scientific and Technical Communicators (ISTC), the British professional body for people engaged in scientific and technical communication (see page 207), believes that British experts, as acknowledged world leaders in technical communication, should be able to provide guidance that will be invaluable to technically orientated people both in the industrially advanced countries and, perhaps even more, in the developing countries that are just embarking on their technological revolutions.

With this broad aim, the ISTC has drawn together a team of highly experienced experts to set forth in this book the techniques and conclusions that have been derived from many years of study and practical experience in various sectors of technical and scientific communication. (However, although every endeavour has been made to achieve a broad concensus of professional opinion, the views expressed by individual authors are their own, and do not necessarily reflect the official ISTC policy in every single respect.) To avoid unnecessary repetition of the male and female gender throughout the text, the contributors have simply used the male gender. This should, however, be read as the female gender, wherever applicable, and is used for the sake of convenience only.

In preparing this work, the authors have endeavoured to cover a broad range of needs, from the student preparing for an examination in technical authorship or graphics, to the engineering manager who wants to improve the quality of his product support documentation; from the technical trainee faced with writing his first technical report to the senior scientist preparing a paper for publication by a learned society; from the junior illustrator seeking information on the practical application and cost effectiveness of various types of illustration to the publications manager seeking guidance on quality assurance procedures.

Although in this book we have dealt specifically with the problems of understanding and communication in the English language, these problems are not confined to Britain. Examples similar to those quoted here can doubtless be found worldwide; so much of our advice will also apply to countries where English is not the main language of technical communication.

Fundamental to this work is our well-substantiated conviction that many concepts which initially appear quite baffling, subsequently prove to be really quite simple. Any difficulty in understanding stems more from a confusing explanation than from the inherent complexity of the concept. Likewise, many so-called engineering problems are, in fact, a combination of a technical problem with a communication problem and/or a personnel problem. The three elements can be differentiated as follows: The technical element is one that must be solved by inaugurating or changing a technical process; the communication element must be solved by inaugurating or changing a communication process; and the personnel element must be dealt with by methods designed to influence human behaviour. There are many cases of overlapping and interaction between the three elements, but it is useful to consider them separately, as only in this way can the true importance of each be assessed correctly and the proper remedies applied.

An analysis of a report from an engineer engaged in commissioning a system installed in a large ship showed that out of a total of 51 items mentioned, deficient information was the main cause of 16 problems and a probable associated cause in a further 12 cases!

A brochure issued by INTECOM – The International Council for Technical Communication – lists the following examples of failures and catastrophes resulting from poor communication.

- A space flight fails because an electrician misunderstood his installation manual.
- A metropolis blacks out because power station staff had inadequate documentation dealing with error or defect detection.
- A miracle drug is delayed ten years because the scientist who discovered it wrote an unreadable research report.
- A new product fails because its technical advantages are not made clear to customers.
- A kitchen appliance is not fully utilized, because users cannot understand the instruction book.
- A plant's utilization is only 50% of capacity because of unsuitable or insufficient maintenance and service documentation.
- Several hospital patients die because users of sterilization equipment had an inadequate instruction manual.
- A multinational development project is delayed because of poor communication between participating design groups.
- A machine operator is killed because he could not understand the operating instructions.

If this book prevents just one such event from occurring in the future, our efforts will not have been in vain.

CHAPTER 1

Choosing Language for Effective Technical Writing

by

JOHN KIRKMAN

A WORD ON MY USE OF 'TEXT'

This chapter is about the use of language in effective writing. Conventionally, it might be expected to deal solely with tactics for putting pen to paper (or fingers to keyboard) to produce a paper 'text'. But in modern technical communication, we must enlarge our concept of a 'text' to include presentations on video screens. So, in this chapter, I shall have in mind a wide range of 'texts', varying from letters to be transmitted by Royal Mail or by electronic mail, to instructions/descriptions/explanations to be presented in book form or on a screen.

FACTORS THAT INFLUENCE THE READABILITY OF A TEXT

To write successfully, we must recognize *all* the factors that influence a reader's response to a text. My terms of reference do not allow me to discuss all the factors fully; but I want to mention them briefly, because decisions about language are always related to decisions of other kinds. Language operates in human contexts, in which other factors often play more important roles than language plays.

Every time I receive a text (from a short letter or memorandum to a weighty manual) my response to it begins as soon as I see it. The text may be one that I am expecting or seeking. If so, I begin to assess immediately whether or not it meets my expectations or needs. Alternatively, the text may be one that arrives unexpectedly. If so, I begin to search immediately for information. What is this text? Why has it come to me? What does it seem to offer me? Should I allocate high priority to it in resources of time and attention?

I seek quick orientation. I seek information from a title, from a summary, from a contents list, from clear headings or from easily readable sections of the text itself. All those may be expressed in well-chosen language: but however good that language, I do not respond favourably to the text if I cannot readily *see* the title because it is overshadowed by other information on the front page. I do not respond favourably if I cannot readily assess the potential value of the document's contents because the summary is vaguely descriptive. My first response is influenced more by the writer's decisions about front-page layout and about tactics for summary-writing than by his decisions about accuracy and tone of language.

Indeed, my response is influenced even by the physical appearance of the text. If it looks thick, difficult to handle, full of dense blocks of unattractive type, I am daunted even before I begin to read. Or, if I am expecting a technical manual, and I receive something that looks like a child's comic, I react unfavourably to what seems an inappropriate form in which to receive technical information.

Such reactions are irrational. I *should* judge scientific and technical texts principally by the ease and accuracy with which I draw information from them. But, like everyone else, I react not only to the *accuracy* of a presentation, but also to its *propriety* – to its apparent conformity to my beliefs about what is suitable or unsuitable for a particular communication task, for a particular audience in a particular context. If tactical decisions about form, layout, selection and arrangement of material, rate of unloading of information, type face and type size have been poor, excellent choice of language to express the content will not make me well-disposed towards the presentation. I shall not find the text 'readable'.

Figure 1.1 sets out the most important factors that influence a reader's response to a text. As you read through that list, you will see that many factors have little to do directly with language. They are a mixture of psychological, social and linguistic matters that call for careful analysis of aims, audiences and contexts – of the nature of the human interactions in which we as writers take part.

Fig. 1.1   Readability: factors that affect a reader's response to a text.

MATERIAL	– Familiarity of subject matter to reader
	– Relevance to reader's needs/interests (selection)
	– Conceptual difficulty (pitch)
ORGANIZATION	– Starting tactics: gaining reader's attention; motivating; orienting
	– Sequence
	– Coherence of argument
	– Unloading rate/density of packing
	– Imposition of pattern, emphasis
	– Balance of exposition/illustration/anecdote
	– Redundancy: unnecessary information
	desirable repetition
LAYOUT	– Type face and size
	– Colour
	– 'White' space
	– Headings
	– Numbering
	– Method of citing references
RELATIONSHIP BETWEEN WRITER AND READER	
	– Writer's intention: teaching
	: professionally informative
	: generally informative
	: light-heartedly informative
	: humorously entertaining

Fig. 1.1   continued

<pre>
                              – Reader's motivation to read: learning
                                                           : skimming
                                                           : evaluating
                              – Reader's attitudes: to subject
                                                  : to journal
                                                  : to author
                                                  : to author's background
READER'S SITUATION
                              – Physical state
                              – Physical surroundings
                              – Psychological state (mood/memory)
                              – Reading ability (speed and accuracy)
                              – Social pressures to know/understand/enjoy
LANGUAGE   – Statements/structures (length/complexity)
                              – Choice of vocabulary: verbal/numerical/graphic
                                                    : familiarity – technical
                                                                    words
                                                                    general words
                              – Simplicity/complexity of verb forms and phrasing
                              – Punctuation and paragraphing
                              – Redundancy: verbosity or desirable repetition
                              – Tone created over-all (narrative, explanatory,
                                conversational, lecturing, aggressive)
                              – Accuracy: of grammar/spelling/punctuation
</pre>

In *Effective Writing*,[1] Christopher Turk and I have discussed in detail the planning and preparation that writers should do to be successful in these interactions. Here, it must suffice just to draw your attention to the ways in which different analyses of aims and audiences lead to variations of writing tactics.

Fig. 1.2   A descriptive text.

PUNCHED CARD LISTING UTILITY

5   OPERATION

After the program has been entered, the software pilot lamps 1–4 are displayed (INN–instruction; section 12.3 describes action to be taken in the event of malfunction). The punched cards to be listed, including the trigger card (which must be the lowest card of the deck) are applied to the hopper of the punched card reader P 115, and the SO-key is depressed. The trigger card is read and printed out under a heading 5, 10, . . ., 80 to guide the eye. After a pause, for checking and generating, subsequent cards are read and listed.

After all cards have been read (condition empty hopper prevails) the program jumps to an INN–instruction (program stop) where pilot lamp 1 is displayed. If pilot lamp 1 is not displayed, action as described in section 12.4 may be necessary. After feeding the hopper with new cards, if necessary, and depressing the RELEASE button of the card reader, the operator can decide to depress:

– SO-key if new cards are to be treated in the same way as former cards and no accumulated totals are required;
– S1-key if new cards are to be treated in the same way as former cards, but accumulated totals are wanted;
– S2-key if no more cards are to be read, or new cards are to be treated in a different way.

If no more cards are to be read, the machine can be switched off . . .

Fig. 1.3   A training instruction.

PUNCHED CARD LISTING UTILITY

5   OPERATION

5.1 Using an INN–instruction, enter the program.
    For details of INN–instructions, see section 2.7. Software pilot lamps
    1–4 should be displayed when the program is entered. If they are not, take
    action as described in section 12.3.

5.2 Arrange in a pile the punched cards you wish to list, with the trigger
    card as the lowest card of the pile.

5.3 Place the punched cards in the hopper of punched card reader P115.

5.4 Press the S0-key.
    The trigger card is read and printed out under a heading 5, 10, . . ., 80
    to guide the eye. After a pause, for checking and generating, subsequent
    cards are read and listed. After all the cards have been read, the program
    stops, and pilot lamp 1 is displayed. If pilot lamp 1 is not displayed, refer
    to section 12.4 for details of corrective action.

5.5 When pilot lamp 1 is displayed:
    ● if you have further cards, feed them into the hopper;
    ● press the RELEASE button of the card reader.

5.6 After pressing the RELEASE button:
    ● if you have fed further cards into the hopper, to be treated in
      the *same* way as the former cards, and you DO NOT require
      accumulated totals, press the S0-key, and go to 5.7;
    ● if you have fed further cards into the hopper, to be treated in
      the *same* way as the former cards, and you DO want
      accumulated totals, press the S1-key, and go to 5.8;
    ● if you have fed further cards into the hopper, to be treated in a
      different way from the former cards, press the S2-key, and go to
      5.9;
    ● if no more cards are to be read, press the S2-key; then switch
      off the machine.

5.7 . . .

Fig. 1.4   A prose instruction for an operator's manual.

PUNCHED CARD LISTING UTILITY

5   OPERATION

ACTION	COMMENT
5.1 Enter the program	Use an INN–instruction. Software pilot lamps 1–4 should be displayed. If they are not, see section 12.3.
5.2 Arrange in a pile the punched cards to be listed, with the trigger card as the lowest card of the pile.	
5.3 Place the cards in the hopper of card reader P115.	
5.4 Press the S0-key	After all the cards have been read, the program stops, and pilot lamp 1 is displayed. If it is not, see section 12.4.
5.5 When pilot lamp 1 is displayed: – if you have further cards, feed them into the hopper; – press the RELEASE button of the card reader.	

Fig. 1.4 continued

5.6 After pressing the RELEASE button:
- if further cards have been fed into the hopper, to be treated in the *same* way as the former cards, and accumulated totals ARE NOT required, press the S0-key, and go to 5.7.
- if further cards have been fed into the hopper, to be treated in the *same* way as former cards, and accumulated totals ARE required, press the S1-key, and go to 5.8.
- if further cards have been fed into the hopper, to be treated in a *different* way from the former cards, press the S2-key, and go to 5.9.
- if no more cards are to be read, press the S2-key; then switch off the machine.

5.7 . . .

The texts in Figures 1.2, 1.3, 1.4 and 1.5 are four different versions of essentially the same material, prepared for different purposes and different audiences. All deal with information about the operation of a punched-card reader attached to a computer. The first is intended as part of the *description* of the whole computer system; the second is an *instruction* for relative newcomers to computing, for inclusion in a training manual; the third is an *instruction* for the operator's manual, designed as a terse outline of the procedure for a reader who has some experience of operating computers; the fourth is an alternative to the third, designed to provoke reflection on the relative merits of prose texts and flow charts in presenting *instructions*.

Each version is clear and comprehensible (although they all rely on knowledge gained in the previous four sections of the original text). However, the tone varies from one version to another. The variations in tone were created mainly by varying the choices of language: but the decisions about language were based on careful analyses by the writer of the relationships he wished to establish between himself and the audiences; and those analyses in turn led to decisions about what choice, arrangement and layout of information would 'work well' in each writing task.

Newcomers to the business of writing often feel that subject-matter dictates both form and style: I hope it is clear from these examples, in which the subject-matter is more-or-less constant, that objective, audience and context are the most powerful influences on what we write and how we write it.

Fig. 1.5   *A flow-chart instruction for an operator's manual.*

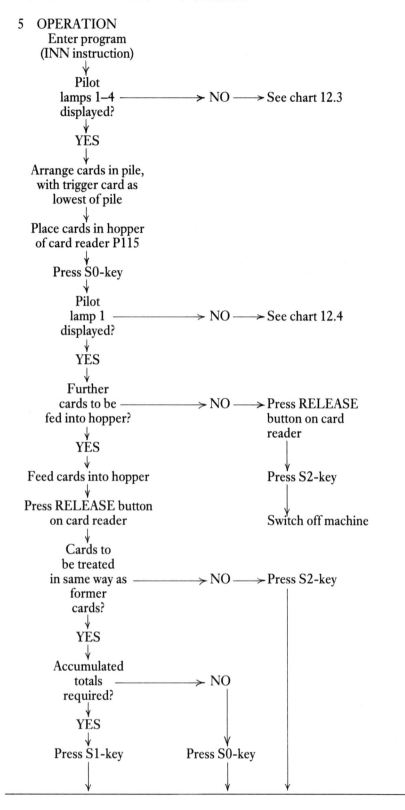

PUNCHED CARD LISTING UTILITY

5   OPERATION

CREDIBILITY AND ESTEEM

Whether we like it or not, readers respond to our writing both objectively and subjectively. They may *try* to evaluate the technical data in our discourse with detachment and objectivity; they may try to concentrate rigorously on the *facts*; but while doing so, they cannot escape *forming an impression* about what they are reading and about the person (or organization) who has written it.

Most of the time, when we read technical documents, we concentrate on understanding what is being said. We are not conscious that we are developing an *attitude* to the information and to the information source. But understanding a fact is one thing: accepting it is another. Acceptance is a matter of attitude.

When I read that the gestation period for a horse is about 11 months, I first comprehend that statement, and then decide whether or not to accept it. Usually, when I am reading scientific and technical documents, I take for granted the reliability of the information sources; that is, I accept the writers as credible. But sometimes my faith in their credibility is shaken. I find an error of logic or fact; or I detect a half-truth or the glossing-over of some incomplete evidence; or I detect that they are using language to obscure an uncertainty or apparently to claim credit unjustifiably. Often, I simply feel that the writer is 'putting on the style' in order to impress me.

When that happens, the writer sinks in my esteem. For example, the content of the following extract is descriptive and non-controversial; but when I read it for the first time, I felt my goodwill ebbing rapidly away from the writer, largely because of the style and tone:

> The animal microclimate is an integrated complexity, whose subdivisions are not distinct entities. It is a commonly appreciated phenomenon that a cold sunny climate is less inclement than a damp, windy climate, though the dry bulb temperatures may be the same. It is therefore imperative that environmental facets be studied under conditions of the strictest possible control of all other microclimatic elements. Thus ammonia pollution was investigated by variation of ammonia concentration within controlled environmental cabinets . . .

In my experience, most scientists and engineers react similarly to excessively formal style. (For evidence, see *Good Style for Engineering and Scientific Writing*.[2]) An excessively formal, roundabout style presumes that we have unlimited resources of time and patience to unravel what the writer is trying to say. Heavy formality is rarely impressive.

Truly *impressive* writing uses language that seems to fit its subject-matter admirably. It seems accurate, incisive, economical and easy to understand. Fortunately, to write in this lucid, plain-speaking way does not call for special skills or even for special techniques. It calls for a 'mental set', a habit of attack on the task of writing that is based on an understanding of the factors outlined in Figure 1.1. The policy for writing that I offer in the following sections is designed to suit that habit of attack. It is designed to transmit information clearly and effectively – to gain credibility and esteem for technical writers.

GENERAL POLICY FOR WRITING READABLY

Two main aspects of the way we 'compose' texts cause difficulty for readers: one is the choice we make of individual words; the other is the way we blend those words into structures – into phrases, clauses and sentences. In general, to reduce the reader's difficulties to the minimum, our policy should be to use 'plain' language wherever possible, and to ensure that the statements we construct are neither too long nor too complex for easy comprehension.

Consider the readability of the following text:

> The radiotherapeutic advantage of administering radiation to patients breathing oxygen at raised pressures largely depends on the assumption that the radiosensitivity of normal tissues is not substantially increased by high pressures of oxygen, whilst a moiety of tumour cells existing as near-anaerobes have their radiosensitivity considerably increased by the added oxygen diffusing into the tumour from the blood during such 'hyperbaric' treatments.

Most readers find the information in this extract difficult to absorb, NOT because it is too specialized for them to understand, but because of the way it is expressed. Too much is linked together in one long statement; and too much of the vocabulary is unnecessarily 'heavyweight'.

For example, *administering* is used instead of *giving*; *substantially increased* is used instead of *much increased*; *moiety* is used instead of *some*, and *hyperbaric* instead of *high-pressure*. Do the 'heavyweight' words carry more meaning than the alternatives I have suggested? If they do, they have value; but I doubt if they do, and I certainly doubt if they carry enough extra meaning to justify making readers handle the extra weight of syllables. The following version, in plainer, more manageable language, carries the same meaning, yet is much more readable:

> In radiotherapy, the advantage of giving radiation to patients breathing oxygen at raised pressures largely depends on one assumption: that high pressures of oxygen do not much increase the sensitivity of normal cells to radiation, whereas they *do* increase the sensitivity of some tumour cells which are near-anaerobes. Sensitivity increases because added oxygen diffuses into the tumour from the blood during high-pressure treatments.

CHOOSING WORDS

Our over-riding objective in writing about science and technology must be to convey meaning accurately. Accordingly, in any debate about whether one word would be shorter, plainer or more readable than another, we must always first establish whether the words have near enough the same meaning for the given audience and context. For example, I do not believe *utilize* and *use* carry different meanings for most readers, so I would always advocate the choice of *use* in technical writing; I do not believe *deleterious* means more or less than *harmful* to most readers, so I would always advocate the use of *harmful* in technical writing; but there are many occasions on which to change *rectify* to *correct* would be to alter seriously the technical meaning of the statement. To make such a change automatically on grounds that *correct* would be shorter and plainer would be disastrous.

In most technical writing, use of a great many 'heavyweight' words is unavoidable. If we are writing about *austenitizing* or *electrophoresis*, we have no alternative but to use those terms (with clear definitions, if necessary). In revising the passage about radiotherapy, I considered the term *'near-anaerobes'* to be essential. An *anaerobe* is an organism that can survive in the absence of free oxygen. Readers for whom the text was intended would have known that definition; for me to have struggled to find another way of expressing the meaning of *anaerobe* would have been tiresome for those readers; I would have had to use a longer expression, and I might have reduced the precision of the statement. Accordingly, *near-anerobe* stayed in my revised version.

My point about vocabulary in scientific and technical writing is that we should avoid *unnecessary* specialist jargon and *unnecessary* heavyweight words. There is no virtue in using *manifests* if *shows* expresses the same meaning adequately; there is no benefit to be gained from writing: '. . . the concrete deck and its steel beams were examined only adjacent to the abutments' if 'next to the abutments' or 'around the abutments' would adequately express the meaning.

Indeed, since use of many heavyweight words is unavoidable, there is distinct benefit to be *gained* from consciously looking for opportunities to write plainly:

DON'T WRITE . . . The ABC assay was successful in identifying the presence or absence of LPS in the separated fractions. The presence of LPS was manifested by a low antibody titre when LPS was incorporated in the diluting buffer, while at the same time exhibiting a high titre in the absence of the 'inhibitory' LPS.

WRITE . . . The ABC assay showed whether or not there was LPS in the separated fractions. The presence of LPS was shown by a low antibody titre when the diluting buffer included LPS, and by a high titre when no 'inhibitory' LPS was included.

By consciously adopting this style, we reduce the 'weight' of what we give our audiences to read. You may think that to take account of the number of syllables we ask our readers to handle is to become far too fussy about linguistic choices. Of course, when we consider the 'heaviness' of individual words like *utilize* and *use*, it is clear that occasional use of *utilize* instead of *use* is not going to ruin the readability of a text. But it is the *cumulative* effect of attending to many small matters like this that makes writing readable rather than unreadable. I cannot suggest in this chapter just one major thing to do to transform your writing dramatically. I *can* offer you many small pieces of advice on tactics that *cumulatively* will produce readable writing.

So, pay attention to the weight and familiarity of the language you use for your given audience. Undoubtedly, as readers become accustomed to handling individual heavyweight words, those words seem easier to handle. The word *electricity* (five syllables) is a heavyweight word, if we judge it on number of syllables alone. But 'heaviness' is derived not only from number of syllables but also from what we can call the 'information load' carried by a word – from the difficulty and familiarity of the concept it expresses.

Most of us are familiar with the basic idea expressed by the word *electricity* (although few of us could define it rigorously!), and since it is a word we meet fairly frequently in daily life, we are not too surprised when we meet it in a text. We identify it without conscious effort, and move on rapidly to see what words lie ahead in the rest of the statement. But when we meet a word that we are not accustomed to handling, we are obliged to halt and to examine it for a little longer than usual. We 'work out' what it means, and then move on. If a text contains many words that make us halt to 'work out' what they mean, we gradually feel a sense of struggle.

Often, we recognize that the writer was obliged to introduce terms unfamiliar to us: part of the task of acquiring new information is the learning of new terms to express that information. But equally often, I feel that I am having to work unduly hard to 'get at the meaning' of a text. I feel that other words could have expressed the meaning equally well, and would have demanded less effort on my part. No doubt you have sometimes felt the same. Try to prevent *your* readers feeling that they are having to work unnecessarily hard to get at the meaning of your text:

DON'T WRITE . . . This allows the disk drives to be allocated between two disk processors giving an advantageous throughput enhancement as well as permitting up to twelve disk drives to be connected.

WRITE . . . This allows the disk drives to be allocated to two disk processors, increasing throughput usefully, and enabling up to twelve disk drives to be connected.

DON'T WRITE . . . Evidence was gained on a visit to the ABC works, where demonstration of fault indication on electricity supply failure was witnessed.

WRITE . . . We obtained evidence when we visited the ABC works, where we saw a demonstration of how faults are indicated when the electricity supply fails.

SLANG AND COLLOQUIALISMS

Let me emphasize that I am in no way advocating loose, slangy, 'matey' diction. Slang and colloquialisms are usually inappropriate for scientific and technical work, because they are imprecise. They rely on shared understanding of background and nuances. In a conversation with a colleague, while you are both looking at a site plan, and can point to it as you speak, you may reasonably say:

'. . . the architect has sited the raw mill *out on a limb* . . .'

but in a written report, it would be unwise to use even such a well-known colloquialism, because its precise meaning is not clear without the gesture and accompanying exchange of glances that make it acceptable in speech. As you stand by a computer, you may say to an experienced operator:

'. . . if the light is flashing, *hit* the ACKNOWLEDGE button . . .'

but in a technical manual, designed for a wide readership, perhaps including many operators for whom English is a second language, that colloquialism would be too vague for reliable communication.

Here are some other expressions from technical documents, all too loosely colloquial for reliable technical communication (my italics):

'... we feel that company X *has the edge on experience* in designing precalciner systems ...'

'... but further investigation is needed into *the pros and cons* of the alternatives ...'

'... there will be *a large civil engineering impact* on the price ...'

'... instrument models X, Y and Z *are tailored* to accept input signals ...'

'... ink wheels *are good for* several months of normal printing ...'

Language must be used with maximum accuracy in technical writing. It is especially important to avoid colloquialisms in documents that will be read by people for whom your language is a second or foreign language. Consider the clarity to overseas readers of these extracts (my italics):

'... the need for *a decent packaging material* becomes more and more necessary ...'

'... location A and location B should also *watch* the A:B ratios ...'

'... ageing tank T2204, first in the series, had *a rather uniform* thickness of about 0.5 inches. The tank surface near the base on the west side was so severely pitted on the outside that no thickness determinations could be made. The insulation around tank 2204 *was quite wet*, either from rainfall or from *minute* quantities of seepage through welds or small holes ...'

Local jargon and abbreviations must be avoided too. Will your audience recognize without difficulty such expressions as:

'... using a *potmeter* ... (potentiometer)'

'... place the *sw.* in the ON position ... (switch)'

'... ensure that the *wng lt* is lit ... (warning light)'

'... this counter registers per trunk the number of impulses, each time an outgoing call *seizes* a trunk ...'?

Even an expression such as: '... can improve beam focus, particularly with doughnut or multi-spot beam propagation ...' will cause difficulty for readers who are unsure whether a standard doughnut is solid (and filled with jam or jelly) or has a hole in the middle!

WRITING FOR INTERNATIONAL AUDIENCES

Writing for international audiences calls for special control over vocabulary and phrasing. Readers for whom English is a second language may have difficulty in detecting the different nuances you wish to convey by using a range of verbs such as:

place
position
locate
instal
fit   ... the plate on ...
mount
fix
put
apply

Do you wish your readers to do different things when you write: *power up*, *turn on*, *connect up*, *plug in*, *apply power to* an electric appliance? Do you wish to convey the same meaning when you tell readers to '*observe* the regulations' and when you write '*observe* the change in temperature'? What do you mean when you write:

'. . . carefully *lower* spindle into frame . . .'
'. . . *lower* back pressure of all output . . .'
'. . . the *lower* speed is used . . .'

'. . . for *straight* mineral oils . . .'
'. . . marks are in a *straight* line . . .'
'. . . the adaptor should have the *straight* side up . . .'

Two other features of choice of vocabulary are vital for clear communication to international audiences: consistency within documents, and standardization of terminology throughout the documentation of your organization. Be careful not to write 'moves towards the bowl periphery' on one page, and 'moves towards the bowl wall' on the next. Don't write 'the mill has had considerable down-time' on one page and then 'the mill has a low service factor' on the next page. Avoid calling a fastener a *latch* on one page and a *lock* on the next. Use *one* term consistently in your documents; be careful not to use *a video tube*, *a CRT*, and *a picture tube* in different manuals.

Remember that there are even differences in British English and American English. I astonished one American technical writer when I pointed out that in Britain, we do not run a current to *ground*, we run it to *earth*. Three other writers were surprised to hear that the term *decal* is not in the *Shorter Oxford English Dictionary*, and is not in general use in Britain. To them, it was a familiar term for a label or sticker, usually a label made to be transferred to glass or plastic from a specially prepared paper. A technical document written in the USA spoke of digging tunnels in the *dirt*; in British English, we should have written *earth* or *soil* or *ground*. In American English, writers *pry off* a cap: in British English we *prise* it off. A *regular* transmission in a technical document from the United States is likely to mean a *normal* or *usual* transmission. In British English, *regular* is likely to be interpreted to mean 'recurring at repeated or fixed times or intervals'. If a British writer sends a memorandum asking for a matter to be *tabled* at a meeting with his American colleagues, he will find the matter postponed for later discussion, or removed from consideration indefinitely – exactly the opposite of what he wants!

My point is not that British English is 'right' and American English is 'wrong'; I am stressing simply that they are different. I am stressing that our analyses of objectives, audiences and contexts must go into considerable detail before we begin to write.

PHRASING

The way we combine words into phrases needs as much care as we give to our choice of words, for two main reasons:

- unusual phrasing – phrasing that differs from the norms of day-to-day expression – seems stiffly artificial to readers, and contributes substantially to the feeling that technical documents are 'heavy going';
- complex word groups can be difficult for readers to comprehend.

A major cause of difficulty in technical writing is excessive 'pre-modification' (the piling up of modifying words in front of a noun). For example:

'. . . a balanced ring trip detector input . . .'
'. . . a complex frequency error correction procedure . . .'

Such chunks of linked words are difficult to digest. The reader has to keep eyes and mind open while waiting to perceive the whole related group *before* being able to work out how all the words are meant to modify one another. Also, the reader's sense of struggle is heightened by the fact that stringing so many modifiers together in front of a noun is not a normal practice in everyday non-technical speech or writing. I suspect that you would find it unusual and clumsy if someone spoke or wrote to you about:

'. . . a decorated playing card holder lid . . .'

Do these words mean that the playing cards are decorated, or the lid? The normal way of expressing that idea more manageably and without ambiguity would have been:

'. . . a decorated lid for a playing card holder . . .'

In normal speech and writing, when we have two or more modifiers to add to a main noun, we usually put one or two in front, and the remainder afterwards. We take the two modifying ideas, *a decorated* and *for a playing-card holder* and place one on each side of the main noun, *lid*. Following that normal practice, we should present the technical statements as:

'. . . a balanced input for the ring-trip detector . . .'
'. . . a complex procedure for correcting frequency errors . . .'

The main justification for recommending this style in technical documents is that it is the normal way of arranging phrases in English, and therefore does not seem artificial or 'heavy going' to readers. But there is another important justification. When a noun is heavily pre-modified, it is not always easy to see whether the pre-modifying words are meant to relate to one another, or individually to the main noun. For example, would you expect a pamphlet entitled *Guide to Successful Rabbit Raising* to give you advice on how to raise successful rabbits, or on how to raise rabbits successfully? Would you expect this statement from a technical report: 'This would leave the six 514 machines dedicated to rectangular hole production', to introduce a statement about rectangular production of holes or about production of rectangular holes?

Perhaps those examples were sufficiently amusing to be entirely clear. But how would you interpret the arrangement of words in the following technical statement: 'The raw mill gas flow regulation valve sequence has yet to be designed'? Are all the pre-modifiers meant to modify *sequence* individually? Is this a statement about a *raw* sequence, a *mill* sequence, a *gas* sequence, a *flow* sequence, a *regulation* sequence and a *valve* sequence? No. *Raw* is meant to be attached to *mill*, *gas* is meant to be a compound with *flow*, and *regulation* is meant to be related to *valve*. The writer wanted to say that the sequence of valves to regulate gas flow in the raw mill has not yet been designed.

Note how much easier it is to absorb his statement when the first item of the group is the main noun, *sequence*. We register first that it is a *sequence* that he is talking about. Then we attach comfortably the facts that it is a sequence *of valves*, and that these valves are to *regulate gas flow in the raw mill*.

The original could be improved slightly by the addition of some commas and hyphens: 'The raw-mill, gas-flow-regulation valve sequence has not yet been designed'. But that would still be clumsy writing. The arrangement that places the main noun *sequence* early in the group is more normal in English, and seems more comfortable to most readers.

Similarly, the addition of a hyphen in *Rabbit-Raising* would improve the title of the pamphlet on rabbits; and the sentence about holes would be improved by the addition of a hyphen between *rectangular* and *hole*; but the addition of hyphens still leaves readers to absorb large chunks *before* arriving at the main nouns they have to decode. Rearrangement to *Guide to Successful Raising of Rabbits* and 'This would leave six 514 machines dedicated to production of rectangular holes' is much more comfortable as well as unambiguous.

Expert readers (expert both in the subject-matter and in the reading of English) develop the ability to span three or four words at a time as they read. They can therefore comfortably read and understand small clusters such as *landing-gear system, cool-start solenoid valve, magnetic fuel-level indicator*. But even expert readers find it difficult to process long strings of words such as: '. . . outer wing-tank diaphragm-actuated-type shut off valves . . .', especially if punctuation signals are omitted. Less expert readers (less expert both in the subject-matter and in the handling of English), who use a slower, word-by-word processing strategy, have special difficulty with such strings of words. Since so many technical documents are now produced for international distribution, it is wise to use a 'rule of thumb' that restricts writing to not more than two pre-modifiers wherever possible.

USE OF 'NOUN CLUSTERS'

In particular, it is wise to avoid confusion when you use a noun to modify another noun. In English, a pre-modifying noun, normally (not always, but normally) is equivalent in meaning to a post-modifying *of*-phrase:

waste disposal = disposal of waste
water repellency = repellency of water
grass cutting = cutting of grass
team selection = selection of the/a team

For this reason, when we see signs outside a factory, 'CUSTOMER RECEPTION' seems normal (= reception of customers) but 'CUSTOMER PARKING' raises a smile (= parking of customers!). In general, it is more accurate and more readable if you use *of*- constructions instead of excessive pre-modification of nouns:

DON'T WRITE . . . enables traffic handling optimization . . .

WRITE . . . enables optimization of traffic handling . . .

OR BETTER . . . enables optimum handling of traffic . . .

DON'T WRITE . . . influences measurement accuracy . . .

WRITE . . . influences accuracy of measurement

DON'T WRITE . . . is used for interrupt handling . . .

WRITE . . . is used to handle interrupts . . .

DON'T WRITE . . . methods for file updating . . .

WRITE . . . methods for updating files . . .

DON'T WRITE . . . to prevent thermostat operation . . .

WRITE . . . to prevent operation of the thermostat . . .

DON'T WRITE . . . is important in sub-station site selection . . .

WRITE . . . is important in selection of sub-station sites.

Noun clusters can cause considerable difficulties, especially for translators. What are the meanings of the following expressions:

ORIGINAL . . . 'system for automatic land vehicle monitoring . . .'
? = . . . 'automatic monitoring of land vehicles . . .'
? = . . . 'monitoring of automatic land vehicles . . .'

ORIGINAL . . . 'extracts data from the failed primary controller memory . . .'
? = . . . 'from the failed memory of the primary controller . . .'
? = . . . 'from the memory of the failed primary controller . . .'

PREPOSITIONAL PHRASES

One reason why noun clusters cause difficulty for readers is that pre-modifying nouns often come between a preposition and its true 'complement'. A preposition normally introduces ('governs') a noun, a noun phrase or a clause (such as a *why-* or an *ing* clause):

Examples
With	difficulty
At	the door
From	*what* has been received previously
By	lift*ing* the reactor lid

In modern linguistic terminology, the noun, phrase or clause is called the *complement* of the preposition. The normal convention in English is that the first noun after the preposition is the complement. For example, sentence (1) below would seem normal, sentence (2) would seem abnormal:

(1) ambient light and temperature are major influences on *the attentiveness* of pupils in classrooms . . .

(2) ambient light and temperature are major influences on *pupil classroom attentiveness* . . .

Unfortunately, in a well-intentioned effort to economize in the use of words, technical writers have got into the habit of packing nouns between the preposition and its complement, as in (2) above. This causes at least reader discomfort (or better, discomfort for readers!), and at worst, a breakdown in communication:

DON'T WRITE . . . follow the steps for monitor removal . . .

WRITE . . . follow the steps for removing the monitor . . .

DON'T WRITE . . . insert a probe under the high voltage anode rubber shield . . .

WRITE . . . insert a probe under the rubber shield of the high-voltage anode . . .

DON'T WRITE . . . the development of systems for marine traffic control . . .

WRITE . . . development of systems for controlling marine traffic . . .

DON'T WRITE . . . this stage of the project will be followed by control equipment selection and purchase . . .

WRITE . . . this stage of the project will be followed by selection and purchase of control equipment . . .

DON'T WRITE . . . a microscope attachment for specimen viewing and stationary focus spectrum recording . . .

WRITE . . . a microscope attachment for viewing specimens and for stationary-focus recording of spectra . . .

DON'T WRITE . . . readers should be familiar with communications processor operation . . .

WRITE . . . readers should be familiar with operation of the communications processor . . .

DON'T WRITE . . . for call dispersion statistics collection . . .

WRITE . . . for collection of the call-dispersion statistics . . .

'MANAGEABILITY' AND 'DIGESTIBILITY' OF TEXTS

The 'manageability' or 'digestibility' of a text is related to the physical and psychological processes involved in reading. If a text is to seem comfortable to read, the writer must give the reader all possible help with the processes of searching, recognizing, linking and storing involved in 'reading'.

We do not read along a line of print in a continuous flowing movement. Our eyes move along the line in a series of very rapid steps. 'Reading' takes place only when our eyes are still: that is, we 'read' when they are focused momentarily on a given point on a line. Each of these momentary pauses is called a *fixation*.

If reading is to seem comfortable, we need to be able to assimilate rapidly the information our eyes pass back to our minds from each fixation. We need to be able to move from fixation to fixation at a constant speed, not to have to linger longer at some stops than at others because we have difficulty in recognizing what the words mean at some stopping points. Also, we need to be able to keep moving forward. If we have to stop and re-focus on earlier segments of the line, we soon begin to feel that we are having to make special efforts to 'make sense' of the words on the page.

When we start to read a text, we set off along the lines of print with no precise knowledge of what words and structures to expect. Our eyes perceive marks (words) on the page. They pass back details of what they have seen to our minds. In our minds, we search for past experience of the same marks/words and try to recall what they 'meant' on previous occasions. If we have seen and used the words frequently in the past, we have little difficulty in attaching a meaning to the perceived signals; but if we can recall only vaguely what they meant previously, we are uncertain what interpretation to hold in our short-term memories as we wait to receive information about the signals further along the line.

The efficiency with which we gradually build up understanding depends on how easily we can recognize the meaning of each word, and relate it to the accumulated information obtained from the preceding words.

But meaning is not derived from the simple addition of words in sequence: Word 1 + Word 2 + Word 3 + Word 4 . . . Words take on differences of meaning and tone according to how they are related to one another.

The precise meaning of a word often depends on the 'collocation' (placing together) or context in which it is used. For example, we interpret *hold* differently according to its different collocations and contexts in:

'. . . we shall *hold* the firm responsible . . .'
'. . . necessary to get a firm *hold* on . . .'
'. . . should be stored in the aft *hold* . . .'
'. . . if the picture slips sideways, adjust the horizontal *hold* . . .'
'. . . possible to *hold* off corrosive attack . . .'
'. . . allow us to *hold* over our decision . . .'

Without hesitation, we interpret *hold* in the first example as a verb, because it arrives after *we shall*. We have no difficulty in knowing that *hold* in the second example is a noun, because it follows *to get a firm*. But when a sentence begins: '*Hold* screws . . .', we do not know immediately how to interpret the collocation. Should we understand *hold* as an adjective describing *screws*, or should we understand it as a verb? If the succeeding words are '. . . such as the brass screws taken from the base-plate of the grinding machine . . .', we still do not know how to interpret *hold*. We are obliged to keep more and more words in the 'forefront' of our minds until we find another cue that tells us how to interpret *hold* at the beginning of the sentence. Only when we find that cue can we pass back another interpreted group for linking and storage in our short-term memories.

'Hold screws such as the brass screws taken from the base-plate of the grinding machine in reserve, because . . .'

That sentence is grammatical, but is not easily manageable, because the writer has broken into two parts the important group *hold in reserve*. It would have been more considerate writing – more considerate of the readers' comfort – if that sentence had been written:

'Hold in reserve all screws such as the brass screws taken from the grinding machine, because . . .'

We are constantly obliged to hold in the forefront of our minds single words, short phrases or larger word-groups, while we wait to see how they should be interpreted in the light of arrivals from further along the line. Also, we have to try to recall what terms such as *this*, *it*, or *the latter* are referring to from previous sentences. And we have to note special indicator-words (*of*, *to*, *beside*) and indicator endings (-*s*, -*ing*, -*ed*), because they show relationships between words that have been stored already and words that are still to come. When we have to hold too much in mind, reading becomes a struggle.

For example, let us assume that we are about to begin reading a new sentence in a description of some electrical circuits. At the beginning of the sentence, our eyes meet the group: 'This small circuit . . .'. They pass back a message that they have found a recognizable 'subject' group, related by *this* to a circuit mentioned in an earlier statement. So they move on to find what follows.

They find: '. . . will replace . . .'. This is another recognizable group (a verb group), which fits with our expectations about what is likely to follow a 'noun + modifiers' group at the beginning of a sentence.

In our short-term memories, we link those two groups 'This small circuit will replace . . .' and wait for something suitable to follow. We expect (or we predict) another noun group, because customary word-order in English most frequently puts an 'object' group after a verb like *replace*.

Our eyes find '. . . the current . . .'. That seems acceptable; but we are a little uncertain. What meaning should we attach to *current*? Should we interpret it as a noun 'electrical charge' or as an adjective 'present, most recent?' We cannot tell. We cannot pass that group back for storage until we have added more words to create a sensible unit.

What comes next? '. . . will replace the current feed . . .'. Still we cannot be certain of the meaning. Since *current* is followed by the noun *feed*, it looks as if the meaning intended for *current* is 'present'.

We continue: '. . . will replace the current feed transistors in . . .'. Now we have more to work on. Is there such a thing as a 'feed transistor'? No. Then it seems that we have been misled in interpreting *current* as 'present'. Let's try interpreting it as 'electrical charge'. That's better: '. . . will replace the current-feed transistors . . .'. If the writer had supplied that hyphen in the first place, we should not have been misled.

We read on: '. . . will replace the current-feed transistors in . . .'. *In* is a preposition, an indicator-word that warns us to expect a noun to follow, expressing one of several possible types of information (the *Oxford Advanced Learner's Dictionary* lists 18 possibilities), including:

place	(in the garden)
manner or activity	(cut the wire in two)
time	(in the afternoon)
inclusion	(in the first half)
ratio	(one in five)
dress	(in rags)
surroundings or circumstances	(in the cold)
state or condition	(in good repair)
form, shape or arrangement	(in three parts)
method or means of expression	(in writing)

In our sentence, *in* is followed by *line*: '. . . will replace the current-feed transistors in line . . .'. *Line* seems to be a noun indicating place; but then we move to the final two words in our sentence, '. . . interface circuits.'. Having seen these words, we realize that *line* is not intended as a noun following *in* as an indication of place. *Circuits* is the noun that is supposed to be governed by *in*: *line* is intended as a modifier of *interface*. The whole group is supposed to be: '. . . in line-interface circuits.'

At last, we have the whole sentence perceived, passed back, grouped and interpreted:

'This small circuit will replace the current-feed transistors in conventional line-interface circuits.'

I have given this analysis of how our eyes and minds would process a sentence, because I want to emphasize how important it is for writers to learn not only the grammar of English but also the tactics of handling English manageably. Our minds seek constantly to 'close' around recognizable units of information that can be passed back into our short-term memories and held there, ready for linking with units that will arrive later. These units may be single words, two- or three-word groups or multiple-word clauses or sentences. If the writer puts words together clumsily, our search for intelligible groups is frustrated: we have to stop and 'work out' what was meant. For example, we stop momentarily to register that '. . . modular patient monitoring systems . . .' must mean '. . . modular systems for monitoring patients . . .'! If a writer creates long and complex structures, our eyes and minds feel overwhelmed – we cannot 'take it all in at one go'.

So, when we write, we must do more than conform to grammatical conventions and use familiar terms: we must make what we write easy to process – we must make it manageable.

SENTENCE STRUCTURE

Manageability must be the uppermost thought in our minds as we build our words and phrases into statements – into sentences and paragraphs. Broadly, we create sentences in one of two ways:

- by linking phrases and clauses in 'main + subordinate' relationships (complex sentences);
- by stringing together elements of roughly equal importance in a linear chain (compound sentences).

Neither technique of sentence-building is intrinsically better than the other. Both are legitimate ways of creating statements in English, and both can be used with clarity, incisiveness and elegance. But both techniques can be used clumsily. A writer who indulges in too much subordination or 'embedding' of clauses creates complex statements that make overwhelming demands on our short-term memories. We feel we cannot hold on to the convolutions of conditions, parentheses, reservations and assertions all at once. We need to break them into more manageable groups for sorting and storage. If a writer links too many elements in a single chain, we feel that our mental jaws cannot open wide enough to swallow the information that is being rammed in. Eventually we choke, and have to break the meal into smaller 'bites' that are easier to chew, swallow and digest.

So, as you write, take care not to make statements that are too long and/or too complex. Check the 'unloading rate' at which you pass information to your readers:

DON'T WRITE . . . For a write operation, the user system first performs the 3 byte command sequence, as in the read operation and next initiates (asynchronously, if the MDC is operating in buffered mode) an X bytes transfer into the Data Buffer (with X = value of 1 to N × 256; N being the number of sectors to be chained), and then indicates the end of transfer with a TERMINATE command.

WRITE . . . For a write operation, the system:

1. goes through the 3-byte command sequence as in the read operation;
2. initiates an X-bytes transfer into the data buffer;
3. indicates the end of transfer with a TERMINATE command.

In the transfer, X is the value of 1 to N × 256; N is the number of sectors to be chained. If the MDC is operating in buffered mode, the system initiates the transfer asynchronously.

DON'T WRITE . . . However, if plate and washer replacement is carried out regularly to avoid running the grate with plates missing, causing damage to the rest of the grate and thorough maintenance including levelling the grate is carried out during normal kiln stops it would seem likely that several more years life can be gained from the existing grate.

WRITE . . . However, if plates and washers are replaced regularly (to avoid running the grate with plates missing, which damages the rest of the grate), and if the grate is thoroughly maintained (including levelling) during normal kiln stops, the grate will probably last several more years.

OR BETTER . . . However, the grate will probably last several more years *provided* that plates and washers are renewed regularly and the grate is thoroughly maintained. Renewal of plates will avoid running of the grate with plates missing, which damages the rest of the grate. Maintenance must include levelling.

DON'T WRITE . . . After the main fuel valve has closed automatically, the fuel pump will deliver HP fuel via another fuel filter (the FCU pre-filter upstream of the FCU) to the P-governor which in turn will act to supply metered fuel in the required quantities to the fuel nozzles via the fuel divider and fuel manifolds (halves) to be sprayed into the combustion chamber interior by fuel nozzles of the vaporizer type.

WRITE . . . After the main fuel valve has closed automatically, the fuel pump delivers HP fuel to the P-governor through another fuel filter (the FCU pre-filter upstream of the FCU). The P-governor then supplies the required quantities of fuel to the fuel nozzles through the fuel divider and fuel manifolds (halves). The nozzles, of the vaporizer type, spray the fuel into the combustion chamber.

OR BETTER . . . After the main fuel valve has closed automatically, the fuel pump delivers high-pressure fuel through the FCU pre-filter to the P-governor. The P-governor then supplies the required quantities of fuel through the fuel divider to the nozzles (vaporizer-type), which spray the fuel into the combustion chamber.

DON'T WRITE... The minimum at 270°C in the number of defects produced by carbon monoxide reduction of the surface coincides with a minimum in the rate of carbon monoxide oxidation in the temperature range 250°C to 300°C, with a maximum in the amount of hydrogen chemisorbed (4) and also with maxima in the rate of methanol production from carbon dioxide and hydrogen deriving from both the steady state (hydrogen pre-treated) and the transiently more rapid rate (carbon monoxide pre-treated).

WRITE...?

PUNCTUATION

Plainly, the revised versions in the last set of examples have been made more manageable not only by rearranging the ideas and expressing them in plainer language but also by using punctuation more skilfully. Punctuation is another topic that my terms of reference do not allow me to discuss fully; but I want to emphasize here that punctuation is an integral part of the signalling system that we call 'written English': it is not an optional extra! 'Acetone carrying pipework' conveys one idea: 'Acetone-carrying pipework' conveys another. I find it irritating to have to re-read sentences such as:

'... The internal ductwork and the external ductwork supporting steelwork can be removed after the survey has been completed ...'

Certainly, I *can* work out that the writer meant 'ductwork-supporting steelwork'; but I can do so only after going through the whole sentence, and then realizing that my first interpretation was wrong. Provision of appropriate hyphens would have prevented this.

Similarly, I have to read well into each of the following sentences before realizing that I must go back to re-interpret the writer's meaning:

'... describes PAS studies of several organometallic compounds that are used as quasi-one-dimensional conductors and catalysts. In particular quasi-one-dimensional rhodium metal complexes and tantalum metal catalysts mobilized on polymeric microsphere substrates were analysed by Black and White, and ...'
('In particular,...')

'... is designed for optimum signal-to-noise performance. To achieve this computer simulation and optimization has been used extensively ...'
('achieve this, computer')

'... Most chains consist of four stations: a master which transmits at 6f

and "red", "green" and "purple" slaves, transmitting at 8f, 9f and 5f respectively . . .'
('at 6f, and')

Provision of appropriate commas would have prevented misreading.

Readers' eyes and minds can progress rapidly and confidently along lines of print only if they can rely on the punctuation marks with which we signal the logic and rhetoric of our messages. I have discussed tactics for using punctuation in technical writing in *Points on Punctuation*[3]. Let me urge you to follow up that topic there.

WRITING INSTRUCTIONS

I have emphasized that different writing tasks call for different tactics of selection and arrangement of information, and for different choices of language. In the preceding sections, I have made general points about style that should be valid in most types of technical writing. Now let us turn to the choices of language we should make in some specific types of writing. First, the language for clear instructions.

Instructions must be unambiguous and specific. These qualities are derived mainly from clear thinking by the writer about what to say and how to arrange it. The following texts are grammatical and are written in short, manageable sentences, but they are poor instructions:

Example 1 'The receiver can now be tilted backwards, as shown in Figure A, until its flange rests on the two supports. The chain safeguards the unit and prevents it from tilting further than necessary.

Before executing this step, make sure that the chain is undamaged and reliably fixed.'

Example 2 'Mount the interface choke unit on the grating in the rack.

The chokes are to be mounted according to drawing ABC 123456.

Note! Before the chokes are mounted on the grating one No. 9 cable and one No. 19 cable must be connected.'

Note in both examples the errors of sequence, the mixture of instructions and commentary, the failure to specify who is to do things, and the failure to provide '. . . if not . . .' information. These are common faults in technical manuals.

The most important point to note in these examples is that they do not obey the cardinal rule of instruction-writing: that instructions should instruct. To say 'The receiver can now be tilted . . .' (Example 1) is to *describe*. If you mean: 'Tilt the receiver . . .', say so with an imperative verb.

Even to say '. . . one No. 9 cable and one No. 19 cable must be connected' (Example 2), though apparently expressing a clear obligation, is not good enough. By whom must it be connected? If the person who is mounting the choke unit has to make the connection, say so with an imperative verb: 'Before . . ., connect one No. 9 and one No. 19 cable'. Otherwise, the change from imperative form to *must* form may be interpreted by the reader as an indication of change of responsibility.

Virtually all instructions should begin with the imperative form of a functional verb (*raise, lift, turn, remove* . . .); but sometimes, it may be valuable to begin your instruction with:

- a time phrase/clause:
    'When the package arrives at X, change . . .'
- a condition:
    'If the temperature drops more than three degrees, raise . . .'
- a specification of a tool or piece of equipment:
    'Using extractor tool XY12, remove . . .'
- a siting phrase/clause:
    'At Board C, switch . . .'

Take care to avoid vague terms like *select* (does that mean I have a choice?), *replace* (does that mean 'put back' or 'fit a new one'?) and *check* (does that mean just 'look at' something, or 'do' something if a given condition is not being met?). A judge in a court of enquiry is unlikely to be sympathetic if you protest 'Surely anyone knows that an instruction to "check that the valve is closed" means he should close it if it is open!'

Again, a judge is unlikely to accept that 'Acrylonitrile levels *will be monitored* . . .' and 'The flammable solvents *should be stored* in the solvent bin . . .' are sufficiently precise for acceptable instructions. *Will be monitored* can be interpreted as a simple statement of future action; *should be stored* seems to leave an option open.

This is not an acceptable instruction:

'Any space occurring between plates should not exceed 25mm providing there is no risk of persons below being struck by tools or other objects falling through the gangway or platform. Normally, closed plating should be observed.'

In writing instructions, we must take maximum care to ensure that our writing is accurate and explicit.

CRYPTIC, ABBREVIATED WRITING

In many technical settings, we want to be as terse and economical as possible, to save space. This applies generally in technical writing, but especially in writing instructions, writing memoranda and writing for a video screen. In these circumstances, we are often tempted to write cryptically, omitting small words like *a* and *the*.

Unfortunately, this style can leave readers uncertain about what was intended. The following examples from instructions usually make readers pause to confirm their understanding of what was intended:

'. . . voltage values are seen through small windows in panel. Switch
    ranges from 100 to 240 in six stages, and is positioned by turning . . .'
'. . . To avoid damage to the actuator stem, supply air pressure to
    diaphragm must not exceed 15 lbf/in^2 and must . . .'
'. . . Supply current required – 15 amps.'

Does the third example mean: '*The* supply current required *is* 15 amps' or 'Supply *the* current required, *which is* 15 amps'? (In fact, it was the former.) The best policy is always to write everything in full, especially if your documents are likely to have overseas readers. Rarely will you find that your texts become significantly longer.

PERSONAL AND IMPERSONAL WRITING

Finally, in these points about choice of language for specific circumstances, let us focus on language for report-writing. Much report-writing is dull and ambiguous because writers try to strait-jacket the whole report into a single style: they try to use third person, past tense and passive voice throughout the text.

It is usually impossible to write a report wholly in the past tense. Though *most* of a report will naturally look back and focus on what *was* done, almost always there are occasions when the writer wants to talk about generally accepted truths ('and because the gross output from x *is* y, . . .') and that means he *must* move to the present tense (and other tenses) occasionally.

Especially in a *Discussion* section of a report, variation of tense is essential. But be careful to sustain a comprehensible sequence of tenses throughout a given section of your discussion. Here is an extract from a discussion of a scheme for the future: the re-development plan has been approved and is being explained in this report, so the correct tense through most of this section should be *future*:

It is intended that the main pedestrian circulation routes are basically unaltered by the scheme. Pedestrians coming from Hog Hill will travel across the existing High Street Bridge into Someplace, although a crossing is required adjacent to High Grove House. Pedestrians coming from the Wharf area westwards either cross the new route at St Mary Street, or pass under it via the extended footpath on the river bank. Pedestrians will be discouraged from using the new bridge, and for this reason footpaths of only 1m are provided. In other areas, footpaths are to be 1.8m wherever possible. It is felt that in removing trunk route traffic from the existing bridge and St Mary Street, the scheme offers considerable opportunity to improve the pedestrian facilities in the Promenade area. The existing bridge will be restricted to pedestrian traffic only, and the portion of Bridge Street between St Mary Street, and the High Street Bridge will be restricted to essential traffic only. The bridge would be resurfaced to improve its water-proofing and appearance. The paved portion of the Promenade between the existing bridge and the new crossing would be taken up and relaid as grass.

Revised Version

We propose to leave the main pedestrian routes unaltered. Pedestrians coming from Hog Hill will travel across the existing High Street Bridge into Someplace, although a crossing will be required next to High Grove House. Pedestrians moving westwards from the Wharf area will either cross the new road at St Mary Street or pass under it on the extended footpath along the river bank. Pedestrians will be discouraged from using the new bridge, and for this reason, footpaths of only 1m will be provided. In other areas, footpaths will be 1.8m wherever possible.

We think that by removing existing trunk-route traffic from the existing bridge, the scheme offers considerable opportunities for improving the footpaths in the Promenade area. The existing bridge will be restricted to pedestrians, and the part of Bridge Street between St Mary Street and High Street Bridge will be restricted to essential traffic. The bridge will be resurfaced to improve its waterproofing and appearance. The paved part of the Promenade between the existing bridge and the new bridge will be taken up and grass will be put in its place.

To write in the third person throughout a report almost always produces clumsy style and often introduces ambiguity. For example, in the extract above 'It is intended that the main pedestrian circulation routes are basically unaltered . . .' is a clumsy and ambiguous way of expressing 'We propose to leave the main pedestrian routes unaltered . . .'. 'It is felt that . . .' is an unclear substitution for 'We think . . .'. 'It is felt that . . .' leaves ambiguity about who is doing the feeling/thinking!

Of course, there are sections of a report in which it is inappropriate to insert unnecessarily the fact that you personally were involved. In a description of an experimental procedure, it is usually irrelevant – would even give the wrong emphasis – to keep saying *I* or *we* did things. To throw emphasis mainly on the action itself, without reference to the actor, we use a passive construction: 'Reactor A was connected to Reactor B and oxygen at 7 lbf/in^2 was passed . . .'

But this is not to say that you should *never* specify when *you* did something. It would be entirely proper to write 'The vessel overflowed after 15 minutes, so we asked X Department to allow us to divert . . .'. Indeed, to write '. . . so X Department were asked to allow us to divert . . .' would be to write less accurately and less clearly.

To write effectively in reports, set your thoughts clearly on what you were asked to do, how you did it, the results you obtained, and what you conclude/recommend: then write as plainly as you can, using as far as possible the language you would choose if you had the chance to present your account in a face-to-face conversation.

Again, let me emphasize that I am not advocating loose, casual diction. I am saying that it is unnecessary – is often distorting – to strain for a special style for writing reports. In face-to-face conversation, you would be unlikely to use the formal, roundabout expressions in the (genuine) extracts below. What benefit do you feel the writers obtained by using the strained style of the originals? If you think the revisions seem more comfortable and natural, AND express adequately the writer's meaning, draw the obvious conclusion – a style similar to that of the revisions is the style you should strive for when *you* write reports:

ORIGINAL: . . . authorize the insurers to effect a direct payment to X . . .

REVISION: . . . authorize the insurers to pay X directly . . .

ORIGINAL: . . . It has been shown that paraquat toxicity in rats is enhanced by exposure to a 40% oxygen atmosphere . . .

REVISION: . . . We have shown that a 40% oxygen atmosphere makes paraquat more toxic to rats . . .

ORIGINAL: . . . the site has previously been subjected to industrial activity including iron making . . .

REVISION: . . . the site has previously been used for industry, including iron-making . . .

ORIGINAL: . . . venting of the lid through T-valves produced blocks exhibiting good fusion properties at the base . . .

REVISION: . . . venting of the lid through T-valves produced blocks that fused well at the base . . .

ORIGINAL: . . . this mixture effects dissolution of the lignin polymer . . .

REVISION: . . . this mixture dissolves the lignin polymer . . .

ORIGINAL: . . . The purpose of this report is to advise on the condition of and the remedial works required to the concrete casings and supports of the precipitators.

The investigation was undertaken by the writer and Mr J. Brown at the request of Mr W. Smith of Someplace Works and supplements the preliminary inspection carried out by myself on 30th February, 1984.

A thorough external visual inspection was carried out on the three precipitators and various types of cracking of the concrete was present in all the three structures. The cracking can be divided into two types . . .

REVISION: . . . This report describes the condition of the concrete casings and supports of the precipitators, and recommends remedial work. The report is based on a visual inspection made by J. Brown and myself at the request of W. Smith of Someplace Works (after a preliminary inspection I made on 30th February 1984).

On all three precipitators, we found cracking of two types: . . .

PLAIN AND MANAGEABLE WRITING

Throughout this chapter, I have advocated that you should adopt a policy of writing 'plainly and manageably'. I am frequently asked three questions about that policy:

1. Is the extra effort involved in thinking and writing more clearly *really* repaid – does it make *that* much difference?
2. Will such a style be generally acceptable in the scientific and engineering communities?
3. Will use of such a style diminish the credibility and esteem accorded to me by my peers?

I acknowledge that it is difficult to judge the relative merits of styles simply by looking at short revisions of clauses or sentences, so Figure 1.6 gives 'before' and 'after' versions of a longer text. I hope the revised version strikes you as distinctly plainer and more manageable than the original.

In order to reassure scientists and engineers that the style I advocate is acceptable, I have made three surveys among professional scientific and engineering groups, which have all produced clear majorities in favour of plain and manageable style. Full results of those surveys are given in *Good Style for Scientific and Engineering Writing.*[2]

Anxiety about possible loss of credibility and esteem is natural. After all, if we are realistic, we must recognize that some writing (much writing?) has as its main objective the promotion of its writer, not the promulgation of new knowledge. Also, much writing (for example, requests for capital,

YAW CHANNEL

The yaw channel of the autopilot is a self-contained yaw damper system which maintains aircraft yaw stability and also acts to assist the roll channel during azimuth manoeuvres so as to give full roll-yaw co-ordination. The system is basically a velodyne servo controlled by transientized yaw rate signals, which operates a linear actuator in series with the rudder control run. If SB 22–4 has not been embodied an aileron position input is provided to give early rudder application in opposition to any yaw induced by changes in aileron setting and also to prevent the application of opposite rudder during entry to, and roll out from, turns. If SB 22–4 has been embodied the aileron position transmitter is no longer in circuit, thus only yaw rate signals are available to the yaw computer.

The linear actuator driven by the channel servo amplifier contains a tachogenerator and a position pick-off, the outputs of which are both applied to the channel as negative feedback signals. The tachogenerator signal is predominant and therefore the servo amplifier and actuator are a velodyne system, giving rates of rudder movement proportional to demand amplitude. The position feedback signal gives the actuator a centre datum about which it moves in response to longer-term position demands such as the aileron position signal, if applicable.

YAW CHANNEL

The yaw channel is a self-contained system that damps yaw and thereby stabilizes the aircraft. It also assists the roll channel during roll manoeuvres, giving full roll-yaw co-ordination. The system is a speed-sensitive servo, controlled by transientized yaw-rate signals. This servo operates a linear actuator in series with the rudder control run.

If SB 22–4 has not been embodied, an aileron-position input applies rudder early against yaw induced by changes in aileron setting. This position input also prevents the use of opposite rudder during entry to and roll-out from turns.

If SB 22–4 has been embodied, the aileron-position transmitter is no longer in the circuit, so only yaw-rate signals reach the yaw computer.

The linear actuator, driven by the channel servo-amplifier, contains a tachogenerator and a position pick-off. The outputs from these units enter the channel as negative-feedback signals. The tachogenerator signal predominates. The servo-amplifier and actuator are therefore a speed-sensitive system that gives rates of rudder movement proportional to demand amplitude. The position-feedback signal gives the actuator a centre datum, about which it moves in response to longer-term position demands (such as the aileron-position signal, if applicable).

Fig. 1.6   An example of what can be achieved by use of a 'plain and manageable' policy.

or proposals for projects) must present a convincing case and change minds – must persuade and impress in the best sense of those words. It is important that the language used should help to create a sense of conviction and confidence.

In *Does Style Influence Your Credibility?*,[4] Ewa Bardell presents evidence to show that plain and manageable style brings *greater* credibility and esteem than a more formal, heavyweight style.

All the research evidence I have ever seen suggests that plain and manageable writing brings a real return for the effort involved. I hope you, too, will find that to be true.

REFERENCES

1. Turk, Christopher and Kirkman, John, *Effective Writing* (Spon, 1982).
2. Kirkman, John, *Good Style for Scientific and Engineering Writing* (Pitman, 1980).
3. Kirkman, John, *Points on Punctuation* (The John Kirkman Communication Consultancy, Witcha Cottage, Ramsbury, Marlborough, Wiltshire SN8 2HQ, UK, 1985).
4. Bardell, Ewa, 'Does Style Influence Credibility and Esteem?', *The Communicator of Scientific and Technical Information*, ISTC, No. 35, April 1978, pp. 4–7.

CHAPTER 2

Finding the Information

by

Mike Austin

Although circumstances vary according to the type of literature being produced, most authors of technical literature spend much more time researching the facts than they do in presenting them. Inexperienced authors often itch to put pen to paper, but the rule is: *Do not write too soon.* Concentrate first on seeking out the facts then marshalling them into a logical order; when you have done this you will find the actual writing, whether book, article or report, will be comparatively easy.

The factors influencing this all-important research vary so much that it is not possible to cover every aspect of the task; nor is it possible to draw precise guidelines. But what I have done is to describe the points that have proved important in my own experience. I have also consulted colleagues with experience in a variety of entirely different fields, from a small technical publications agency to a multinational radio and electronics company.

Although this chapter is concerned mainly with the extensive research required for comprehensive operating and maintenance manuals on major items of engineering equipment, many of the investigatory processes will apply equally to other types of engineering literature such as sales leaflets or technical articles.

The basic research has two broad objectives; first, to assess what kind of people the readers are likely to be and what their needs will be; second, to obtain the information on the equipment or process that will meet these needs. During the early stages of this research, the basic synopsis will be compiled.

In this chapter these two objectives are discussed separately, although in practice the distinction is not always so clear. Investigation of the components fitted to a piece of equipment will often raise questions as to the user's needs regarding maintenance of those components. What degree of maintenance does the user intend to undertake? Surprisingly, very often no one really pays much attention to such details until publications staff start asking questions. But there is little point in spending a lot of time investigating, writing and illustrating the overhaul procedure for a component if the policy will be to return the component to the manufacturer for overhaul!

WHO WILL BE THE READERS; WHAT INFORMATION WILL THEY REQUIRE?

The starting point for this part of the investigation must be to find out whether the equipment contract refers to a publications specification or otherwise formally defines the publications requirements in contractual terms. This is discussed in Chapter 10. The finance allowed for the production of technical publications must also be ascertained at an early stage, as this may impose overriding restrictions on the scope of the work.

Some engineering publications, such as a motor vehicle handbook, are intended for use by a broad mass of the general public with widely varying degrees of technical knowledge; others, such as the maintenance instructions for a ship's engine, are based on the assumption that the reader will have had, at least, a basic engineering training. Occasionally, as with defence equipment, the reader's precise level of skill and training will be specified.

So one of the first steps in basic research must be to determine precisely what level or levels of ability and comprehension you are writing for. Will all the readers be fluent in English? Will some sections of the book, for instance the basic operating instructions, need to be aimed at a lower level than others?

Having decided on the level or levels of understanding, aim to be consistent. Do not on one page address the reader as if he were an untrained layman then treat him as a skilled fitter on the next – unless of course, the pages are intended for two different levels of personnel, in which case it may be helpful to state this fact.

Be wary of advice that 'you should write the manual as if it were for use by a bunch of morons'. People who make such statements rarely, perhaps never, consider the ramifications of their remarks. Can a moron read an electrical circuit; if not, what is the alternative? A manual written on the basis that the reader has no knowledge would be infinitely large. Only when appropriate assumptions of knowledge are made can the work be given precise and realistic limits. The establishment of such limits is one of the prime tasks of an author's basic research.

In the case of sales literature, the success of the document will greatly depend on whether it answers all the questions potential customers are likely to ask. In determining what these are, seek the opinions of people unfamiliar with the product as well as those of the expert.

Turning now to some of the details that affect presentation, it is important to ascertain what units and symbols should be used. Is it safe to assume that the reader will recognize British Standard electrical symbols, or is an explanatory key required? If the equipment is going abroad, what is the best way to define lubricants and similar materials so that they can be readily identified and ordered locally? Will any of the illustrations or other sections of the manual need to be used for wall charts, microfilm or other purposes? It is important to know this before the illustrations are drawn, in order to select the best type sizes and line thicknesses.

Find out as much as you can about the conditions under which the equipment is to be installed and used. Are installation and commissioning instructions required? Will the equipment be used in unusual environments, for example, extremes of temperature or sand storms, which may affect its operation or maintenance? What arrangements (if any) have been made to allow for possible modifications to the equipment and how will information on this be distributed and incorporated in the technical publications?

The size, cost and configuration of the manual will be greatly influenced by the maintenance policy for the equipment and the associated procedures for provisioning spares. Will components be overhauled in the field or repaired by unit replacement? What overhaul and maintenance facilities does the user have? Facilities that are commonplace in Britain may not be available in some other countries.

Parts Catalogue Requirements

The inclusion of a parts catalogue can provide many pitfalls for the unwary, so it is prudent to consider this very carefully and to agree at an early stage exactly what is required. Clearly the parts catalogue must be closely integrated with the procedure for supplying spares; in the case of a large organization with a complex spares system the type of parts catalogue needed to meet the system's needs will be specified. But even when a publications specification has been quoted, there still can be important variations in interpretation, as anyone with experience with British military parts catalogues will agree! At times, differences in interpretation can have a considerable influence on the cost involved. If, for example, an alpha-numerical part number index has to include the equipment constructor's part number as well as the component manufacturer's part number, this will considerably increase compilation time and, hence, the cost of the index.

Another important point to be resolved is whether exploded illustrations are mandatory or whether other, much cheaper, forms of illustration, such as existing orthographic sections, will be acceptable, providing they enable the parts to be readily identified.

If no particular format of parts catalogue has been specified, then the first question to ask is: Will the parts catalogue cover every single item of the equipment, including every bracket, nut, bolt, washer and split pin, or only the more important items that are likely to be ordered as spares? The former costs very much more than the latter – perhaps ten times as much.

The next fundamental decision is whether the parts catalogue should quote the actual part numbers of every item, as in most military catalogues, or whether it should be based on numbered illustrations with corresponding keys that state the name of each numbered component, but not its part number; as is the practice with many commercial companies. It is useful to consider the merits of these alternative methods.

An illustrated parts catalogue arranged to give the part number of every single component of the equipment, down to the last plain washer, may seem ideal, but it is very expensive and takes a long time to produce. Work on the parts catalogue cannot progress very far until all the detailed drawings have been finished, checked and sealed. As a result the equipment may be in service for quite a long time before the parts catalogue becomes available. Sometimes, several years may elapse between the introduction of the equipment and the arrival of the catalogue! Indeed, intervals exceeding six years, are not unknown in military spheres, when the catalogue becomes entangled with other spares provisioning procedures.

Another problem is keeping the catalogue up to date. Even the smallest modification will involve amendment. This problem is greatly increased if the manufacturers of components make internal changes without notification. In fact, most manufacturers of motors, pumps, valves, gearboxes and similar components reserve the right to do precisely this, which is why they stipulate that the component serial number must be quoted when ordering spares. There is therefore no easy way for the catalogue compiler to monitor the modification standards of components listed in the catalogue, although certain specialized industries, notably the aircraft industry, have rigorous modification procedures which largely overcome this problem.

For equipment produced in relatively small numbers, many, perhaps most, of the components will never be required as spares. No benefit therefore derives from the time spent researching and indexing the part numbers of such components.

The alternative type of parts catalogue (Figure 2.1) is based on a series of illustrations in which each component is given a key number. Associated key lists give the name of each component against its key number. The purpose of this type of catalogue is to enable the user in the field to communicate to the equipment manufacturer precisely which part he requires. Its function is not to identify the definitive part number of the part to be supplied. Ascertaining part numbers is the responsibility of

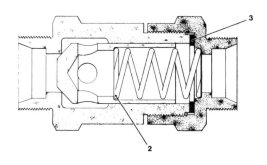

FIG. 2 – VALVE, NON-RETURN

VALVE, NON-RETURN

Fig/Item Number	Part Number	Description	Units per assembly
2–1	**A3/35-4025**	**Valve, non-return, John Doe type XYZ, modified by John Smith (V John Smith)**	**1**
2–2	213312	Spring, helical compression, John Smith Ref 1234, (V J. Brown)	1
2–3	200-019-44	Seal, O-ring, John Smith Ref 5678 (V Bill Doe Hydraulics)	1

The example above gives full details of each item, including the part number of the main equipment manufacturer, the vendor of the item (denoted by the letter V) and the vendor's part number.

The example below only gives the illustration number and the key numbers on the illustration. When the user identifies the illustration and key number, this is sufficient to enable the main equipment manufacturer to identify on his own copy exactly what part is required. In this case the parts catalogue serves only as a means of precise communication between the user and the main equipment manufacturer, and not as a document by which the user can order the part directly.

VALVE, NON-RETURN

Fig/Item Number	Description	Units per assembly
2–1	**Valve, non-return**	**1**
2–2	. Spring	1
2–3	. Seal, O-ring	1

Fig. 2.1   Alternative methods for cataloguing parts.

the equipment manufacturer and his component suppliers who check the modification state of the component, and take into account spares availability and other relevant factors when supplying the part.

The illustration/key number type of catalogue can be produced much more quickly than the comprehensive part number type and, therefore, is much cheaper. Work on the former can start much earlier, because there is no need to await completion of all the drawing parts lists before starting. It is far less liable to amendment due to modifications, because minor alterations that do not change the pictorial shape do not affect the catalogue. Providing the user quotes the component serial number, unannounced internal modifications to components will be allowed for when the manufacturer dispatches the part.

The equipment manufacturer needs to keep an illustration key number to actual part number index for all items likely to be required as spares, and this can be added to as further spares requirements become known. But only the items actually required will be researched and indexed; so no effort will be wasted.

The main disadvantage for the user of the illustration key number type of catalogue is when there is a spares holding of a part which is used in a variety of different types of equipment so that it has several different illustration/key numbers but only one part number. In such cases it may be necessary for the user also to have his own illustration/key number to part number index.

The type of parts catalogue that best suits a particular application will have to be determined after considering all the relevant factors. Sometimes it may be better to quote actual part numbers as well as illustration/key numbers for items included in the recommended spares list for the equipment, but only the key numbers for all other items.

OBTAINING THE INFORMATION TO MEET THE READERS' REQUIREMENTS

In his search for information a technical author needs to be something of a detective, a super-sleuth, constantly probing, questioning and checking. Every piece of information is suspect until cross-checked and verified. Be wary of the person who quotes facts and figures off the cuff; rather rely on someone who checks the records before answering.

A certain reluctance to impart knowledge is not uncommon in certain branches of technology; it would seem to stem from a subconscious reaction to another's apparent encroachment on skill and status. However, a little subtle flattery by the technical author regarding the expertise and status of the informant together with a reassurance that top quality manuals and literature will enhance the prospects of both the company and its employees is probably the best way of overcoming any seeming reticence!

Be very cautious if you are asked to write about something that you will not be able to examine personally or that you do not really understand. To do so is to court disaster. You may be asked to produce modification instructions for equipment that was out of production when you joined the company and which you have never seen. Try not to accept this situation. It may be expensive to travel the length of the country to familiarize yourself with some out-of-date equipment, but you will cost your company a lot more, in terms of goodwill as well as money, if your instructions subsequently prove to be incorrect. The alternative, of commissioning an engineer working in the locality to obtain the information on your behalf, may be cheaper, but you have no guarantee as to the results.

A good technical author is a fundamental thinker. Before he can establish a sound structure for a book or document system, he must have a sound knowledge of what the equipment does, how it does it and its interfaces with associated equipment.

As an example of the importance of fundamental thinking, I cite the case of an author visiting a large ship with the brief to write instructions for draining, refilling and then bleeding the air from an extensive hydraulic system. He was provided with a system piping diagram drawn in plan form. Now for the master stroke! He said to himself: 'Bleeding is a vertical problem'. Whereupon, on arriving at the ship, he roughly sketched the piping diagram in vertical elevation form. Of course, this immediately identified the problem areas and potential air locks, and the rest of his task was easy.

When seeking information for a chapter or article that describes complex equipment, try to establish the functional/physical relationship of the equipment and how you plan to deal with this. Will it be best to separate completely the functioning of the system from its physical construction, or should the two be integrated? If you can establish the functional/physical structure of the chapter in broad terms, this will often assist in determining just what information is required to fill in the details.

For arranging the information for a parts catalogue, a set of coloured pencils is invaluable. First, work out a logical sub-division of the equipment into sections or chapters allocating one colour or combination of colours to each. Next go through all the drawings and parts lists and colour every item or group of items according to whichever chapter or section they belong. Then, when you are ready to begin writing all you have to do is collect and collate all items of the same colour. Similarly, coloured pencils are invaluable for delineating and identifying the elements of complex system diagrams.

The main sources of information available to an author are:

- The actual equipment.
- People associated with the equipment.
- Specifications, drawings and other documents associated with the equipment.
- Literature supplied by component manufacturers.
- Previous literature on similar equipment.
- Text books and articles on related subjects.

First, the actual equipment   Here the in-house author working for a small company has a great advantage. He can, and should, start to take an interest in the equipment at an early stage and watch it grow on the shop floor or in the laboratory. Particular attention should be paid to items that may not be readily accessible later. Observing the build in this way can also be useful when you have to write instructions for the removal and installation of major components. Photographs or sketches made at various stages during the build can also be very useful, and not only to publications staff!

During this period the author should constantly try to identify himself with the potential user and, where necessary, speak out on his behalf. An electric motor installed without an arrow to show the direction of rotation; an inaccessible grease nipple; ambiguous or misleading labels; and discrepancies between equipment and drawings; these are the sort of things for which an author must be constantly on the alert.

When working on a book for a new piece of equipment which has not yet been completed, the technical author may be the first person to link together in an operational context all the various components and systems of the complete unit. In a way, by synthesizing the process in words, he acts as a literary test bed for the equipment. Any errors detected at this stage can be rectified much more cheaply than if not discovered until later.

The people   Everyone who has knowledge or experience of the equipment, from chief designer down to the most junior fitter, is a potential informant for the author. Get close to them; listen to their problems and grouses. They may, for example, indicate the fact that great care needs to be exercised when installing a certain component, or that the drawing is wrong in some particular respect. Sometimes conversation on the shop floor can reveal a hazard or a requirement for a safety instruction that had previously been overlooked.

Remember that co-operation is a two-way process. Technical publications departments usually amass a vast quantity of literature on components and other information, and this should be proffered freely to others. Build up a library in the department, especially a collection of illustrations. A set of photographs taken during a previous build can be invaluable to a fitter about to start building an unfamiliar piece of equipment; he will be your friend for life! Similarly, a copy of an explanatory diagram prepared for a manual will be very welcome to an apprentice trying to understand the operation of a complex unit. As well as improving the efficiency of the company, you will enhance the status of 'tech pubs' and establish lines of communication that will be invaluable when *you* are seeking information.

Interviewing a senior, high-powered executive who is an authority on a particular piece of equipment can be a very daunting prospect for a junior or inexperienced author. Invariably the expert will be a busy man whose time is valuable. Do not rush unprepared into such an interview. Try to find out as much as you can beforehand, otherwise you will not know the important questions to ask or be able to understand the replies. Busy executives have little time to waste on ill-prepared investigators. On the other hand, good co-operation will normally be forthcoming if you have established yourself as someone conversant with his subject who can elicit the information required with a few succinct questions.

But the pre-planning of questions must not be carried too far; there are dangers in having too many preconceived ideas. The pre-planned question can only be based on the questioner's limited knowledge or assumptions. If the person being interviewed just answers the questions, important side issues or even valid counter factors may not be revealed. This situation is most likely to arise with an awkward or reluctant interviewee. On the other hand, if the person being interviewed is allowed to ramble, quite valuable snippets of information can sometimes emerge.

You may easily pick up a lot of seemingly irrelevant material, particularly during early contacts with a new source, but do not be too anxious or quick to discard information of no immediate obvious relevance. It can provide a context which facilitates better judgement as to what really are the vital facts. An overall view of the technical and organizational skeletons can be most useful, and sometimes it is important to discover what *not* to say!

The following incident exemplifies how subsequent rambling can elicit information that goes far beyond and, indeed, is quite different from that anticipated from the initial direct question. On being asked how to perform a particular system flushing operation, a service manager replied, 'That's easy', and then proceeded to list a few simple operations that had to be performed. During the ensuing conversation he happened to mention that his staff took a week to perform the task and that they experienced quite a lot of difficulties. From the subsequent questioning on the obvious discrepancies between the two statements, a very different picture began to emerge. In fact, the procedure proved to be quite lengthy and much more involved than the list of operations originally stated.

To the uninitiated it may be surprising that an engineer who is thoroughly familiar with a piece of equipment, which he even could have designed, may not be able to provide a set of comprehensive and coherent operating instructions. But people who are very familiar with something frequently fail to mention what to them is obvious; and this familiarity may prevent them from seeing the problems from the viewpoint of an inexperienced operator. Often the best method is to write operating instructions yourself and then submit them to the expert. Even if he has to rewrite parts of it, he will be working from the comprehensive and logical foundation that you have prepared, and the end result will very likely be far superior to an edited version of the expert's own efforts.

Ideally, if possible, operating instructions should be checked by having someone unfamiliar with the equipment operate it, without assistance, according to the instructions. It is also useful to operate the equipment yourself, under supervision, if this is practicable.

Specifications, drawings and other documents   The various specifications for the equipment are often a convenient starting point for an

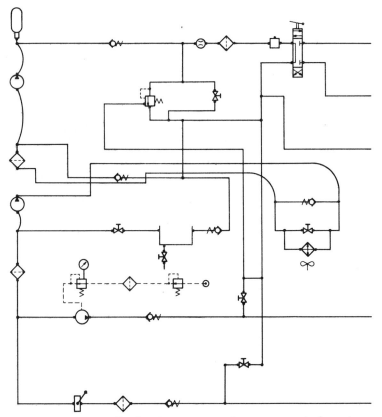

Fig. 2.2   *Section of hydraulic circuit as shown on production drawing.*

investigation, as they state the intended function of the equipment, the main design parameters and other essential data. However, do remember that some of the quoted figures may change as the result of consultations and concessions during the design and development of the equipment.

The next stage is to study the main assembly drawings. If the drawing office has not constructed a family tree showing the relationships of main assembly, sub-assemblies and sub-sub-assemblies, then it is well worth while for the technical publications department to do this. The time spent will be more than recovered later.

If system diagrams are involved, this is the next area to consider. Clear, logical, well-arranged system diagrams are crucial to the understanding of a complex system. Draughtsmen are not specialists in the art of communication, so it is rare to find a flow chart or fluid circuit that will meet the high standards expected of technical publications. Redrawing the main flow diagrams and circuits in logical and fundamental form is often the first step to achieving a real insight into the functioning of equipment involving complex systems. Figures 2.2 and 2.3 illustrate part of a hydraulic circuit as shown on the production drawings compared with the same system redrawn in logical order by the technical publications staff.

For systems with a complex electrical control system, the best way to gain a basic understanding can be to work through the complete set of system circuits and write out the functions/sequence in step-by-step form. For example, press the start button; relay RL1 is energized and locked on; contact RL1/1 energizes RL2 and so on. Apart from teaching you how the system functions, this will identify all the interlocks which affect operating procedures, as well as the safety systems, warning indications and many other fundamental features. This initial rough write-up will also become the basis of your description of the control system. Sometimes this type of information is better arranged diagramatically.

Technical publications staff must always remember that design or production drawings perform a different function from equipment manuals, and standards that may be suitable for drawings used internally may not necessarily be appropriate for users in the field. Do not blindly follow drawings; for example by copying circuit symbols that do not conform to

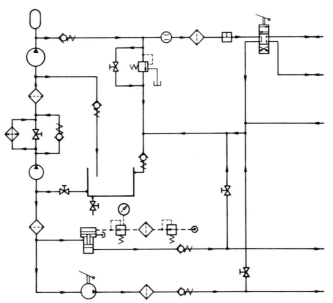

Fig. 2.3   Same section of circuit as redrawn for technical publications.

British Standards. At times the drawing office may not be able to supply all the system diagrams required by the publications department. They may not have prepared a physical wiring diagram although for the user in the field this will be extremely useful, if not essential. In such situations, the publications department must take the initiative and draw its own diagrams. The terminology used on drawings may also have to be altered to eliminate inconsistencies and facilitate understanding.

Much technical publications time is wasted because of the inadequacies of internal documents used for source information. But how many authors do anything positive to rectify this situation? Always report back to senior design and development staff any weakness found in formal documents. Although it will not help your immediate problem, by constantly highlighting such weaknesses the required information may become available automatically in the future. As a skilled communicator you have much to offer in improving internal as well as external documentation.

Manufacturers' literature   The product support literature provided for industrial components can vary from very good to utterly useless. Regrettably, even now, there are large industrial organizations with names that are household words throughout Europe whose product support literature is disgraceful. These organizations just do not seem to comprehend the enormous amount of wasted time and the number of engineering problems that stem from deficient product support literature.

Very often leaflets are supplied which are the last of a long series of copies made from copies, so that much of the detail has been lost. Illustrations are reduced so small that details are no longer legible, instructions are difficult to read, and vital information is lost.

Another common fault is for the literature to cover a number of similar models without any clear distinction as to which applies to the actual model with which you are dealing. Even worse, firms will sometimes send literature covering a similar but not identical model because they do not have anything covering the actual model specified.

Whenever circumstances permit, carefully vet all literature supplied by component manufacturers. Most important of all, ensure that it applies to the equipment that you are dealing with, *not* to something similar. If information is difficult to understand, deficient or suspect, do not be afraid to query it. If a manufacturer states that a component must not be dismantled, find out why, so that you can advise your readers – perhaps special equipment is required or hazardous operations are involved; the fact that dismantling would invalidate a guarantee may not be the deciding factor.

If you are producing a high quality manual, it is likely that some of the component literature supplied will not fully meet your needs. It will be necessary to go back to the manufacturer and request drawings and further information. In the last resort, it may even be necessary to have a component stripped down in order to produce an accurate illustration and find out exactly how it is constructed. Although these comments apply mainly to mechanical components, authors working in the electronics field also experience difficulties because of inadequate literature supplied by component manufacturers.

Previous literature   Few items of engineering equipment are absolutely conceptually new. Very often manuals and other documents will have been produced for equipment similar to the one that you are dealing with. Obviously, such existing material will be very useful, but again a word of caution – do not be scared of rewriting or redrawing anything that does not conform to your own high standards. And when adapting a previously written passage, be especially careful to check the small items; errors of detail are much more likely to occur when adapting a passage than when writing from scratch.

Text books and articles on related subjects   Anyone writing a technical article or report on a specialized subject is almost certain to be conversant with the literature that could be relevant to his needs.

For authors seeking more general technical information, in Britain, the public libraries and the specialized libraries of organizations such as the Patents Office and the professional institutions provide a superb service.

Industrial, commercial, academic and administrative bodies that frequently need the services of information technology specialists can join the Association of Special Libraries and Information Bureaux (ASLIB), 3 Belgrave Square, London SW1X 8PL. For a modest fee, depending on the size and type of organization, ASLIB provides its members with:

- Advice on information problems and information handling techniques.
- On-line computer searching on a wide range of data bases.
- A range of publications relevant to information technology.
- Assistance with translations, including an index of unpublished translations and a register of specialist translators.
- Services to the information profession, including a major collection of books devoted to special librarianship and information science.
- Assistance in the recruitment of professional information staff.
- Document location and identification.
- General help and advice on all aspects of the application of modern information technology.

COMPILING THE SYNOPSIS

During the early stages of the foregoing research the main subject headings and summaries of contents can be determined, together with a provisional list of the associated illustrations. This information is then arranged in accordance with the selected or specified chapter arrangement (*see* Chapters 3 and 10) to form the basic synopsis of the book. From this synopsis the amount of work can be estimated and the costs calculated.

CHAPTER 3

Contents and Presentation of Technical Manuals

by
John Wakeford

INTRODUCTION

Unlike the technical article in a popular engineering journal or magazine, which is read for its interest value, or the information given in a textbook, which is read in order to learn, the technical manual is given only the briefest glance on receipt and then put on a shelf. It is a reference book, and is retrieved only when information is sought about the equipment it supports. Moreover, it is opened only at pages dealing with specific areas of the equipment or describing certain procedures that affect the equipment. To find those pages quickly, the reader will obviously refer to the list of contents provided at the front of the manual.

It is in the list of contents that a 'behind-the-scenes' view of the overall manual is glimpsed – its exposition. If the manual has been well planned, its list of contents will reveal its structure and, in turn, reflect a logical presentation of the equipment it deals with. At the same time, the reader is quickly informed where to look within the bulk of the manual; the rest of the manual is of no interest to him.

The pages containing the sought-after information are now all-important. For the reader, with his particular need for information, the pages he now studies *are* the manual; the total manual will stand or fall depending on the lucidity and effectiveness of those pages.

Prime Objectives While writing the manual, the technical author is not concerned with the 'roulette' problem of which pages will or will not be read; his task is to ensure that every page informs, and that each gives the reader confidence. He achieves this by observing several disciplines. Some of these are described in this chapter; others are discussed elsewhere in this book.

Chief amongst these disciplines are: an in-depth understanding of the equipment to be written about (resulting in a comprehensive but meaningful contents breakdown) and an appreciation at all times of who he is writing for. Such appreciation will influence his presentation while writing the various topics of the manual.

FIRST STEPS – THE BRIEF

Before any attempt is made at planning an equipment manual, the technical author must know if a specification or an approved 'house style' is to be followed. As discussed in Chapter 10, any such specification will give indication of the order of contents and their depth of treatment, and will also give the presentation format (which includes page size, typeface to be used, and typeface area).

If no mandatory specification is to be followed, the author must discover exactly what kind of publication is required: an operator's handbook, a maintenance (or workshop) manual or an illustrated parts catalogue. He must also be advised about the ultimate use and intentions of the book, because some publications may serve more than one purpose. For example, an operator's handbook may be presented as an attractive benefit by the sales team when demonstrating the equipment, and may also be used in the classroom for product-training purposes.

All these details are learned at the first stage of the manual's preparation – the briefing or 'brief'. This is a most important stage; not only does it lay the foundations for the content and presentation of the intended publication, but it also determines points of contract and areas of costs.

Questions to ask at the Brief   Some people are very good at providing briefs, giving the essential facts and details in concise, unambiguous statements which, in turn, prompt the author to ask questions that give more detail and a better understanding of the requirements. Unfortunately, there are also some who are inapt at giving a brief, and the poor author has to listen to a lot of words and anecdotes that are irrelevant to the required facts. In this case, the practised (and patient) author will politely steer the briefing by asking such questions as:

What kind of manual?   An operator's manual and a maintenance manual each have their own style of presentation (details of which are given later). Each also differs from the other in the depth of treatment, affecting both the timescale of preparation and the cost. This question also prompts the next:

When is the manual required?   All writing projects must have a time-scale, terminating at that dreaded moment – the 'deadline'. This constraint serves to discipline the author (as well as the handbook team of illustrators, photographers, typists, etc.) to the fact that the production of a book is like the manufacture of an item of hardware, and that someone is waiting to receive the finished product. Very often, the author will be dealing concurrently with other projects, and must organize his time accordingly if he is to handle the new project within the requested time-scale. Even so, the time-scale must be realistic for the task being undertaken – an operator's handbook for a nuclear power station cannot be adequately written in three weeks!

Is the subject equipment available?   Actual viewing of the equipment by the author is invaluable if he is quickly to obtain a firm grasp of what it is about, what it does and what it does not do. He can quickly determine the breakdown of its assemblies and sub-assemblies, and can therefore more easily translate such a breakdown into sections and chapters, as well as assessing the quantity and type of illustrations that will be needed.

And when the manual is started, any problem areas of description, or details of disassembly can be very readily resolved by simply looking at and handling the equipment. Provided that any necessary permission is given, the author should take snapshots of the equipment. Not only are these of help when he is at his desk, but can also serve as the basis for illustrations.

Who is the engineer to be contacted for information?   This person is going to be the author's prime contact, to whom he should be introduced as early as possible. From him, the author will discover who his colleagues are, which of them should be primed for specific kinds of information (e.g. mechanical, electrical, electronic, etc.) and the best time of day to visit them.

Who is the draughtsman to be contacted for information?   The best initial source of information is obtained from the drawing office. But the author must know if the drawings are up to date and conform to the final production standard of the equipment (which is the standard to which the manual is normally written). Viewing the drawings (not all of them but those selected from the drawing list) will give the author ideas of the equipment breakdown and the type of illustrations he will use.

Is there a manual on a similar equipment?   If there is, then looking through it will perhaps give guidance as to the required scope and content. It may also highlight areas which should have been dealt with in greater depth, or reveal inadequate coverage by illustrations.

What format size is the manual to be?   Unless an unorthodox format is required, the standard format will be A3, A4 or A5. This information is most important to the presentation of the manual since it determines the final text and illustration areas (see Figure 3.4). Examples of the use of these three formats are:

A3 (297 × 420 mm): usually used as a supplement to maintenance or workshop manuals to contain large illustrations, especially circuit diagrams.
A4 (297 mm × 210 mm): the most frequently used format for manuals. (This book is produced to A4 format.)
A5 (210 mm × 148.5 mm): this format is usually adopted for small-content manuals. It may also be used as a supplement to a larger book, serving as a pocket-size compendium of operating instructions, performance graphs, tables, etc.

Note that when quoting page sizes, the side dimension is (by definition) quoted first. Thus, in the dimensions given for A4, 297 mm is the side (or height) of the page. A look at the previously-mentioned dimensions will show that A5 is half of A4, and A4 is half of A3. By doubling the shortest dimension, therefore, A3 progresses up through A2 and A1 to A0, which is the standard (ISO) 'board' milled.

How will the manual be printed?   The kind of printing process to be used will have a significant bearing on the type of master material to be prepared. For example, the economics of printing only a few copies of the manual would suggest its being printed by one of the plain paper (electrostatic) processes. In this instance, it is wise to ensure that only line illustrations are used since the electrostatic process does not reproduce half-tone pictures as crisply as conventional printing processes (offset lithography, for example). Details of the various printing processes are given in Chapter 7.

The answers to the foregoing questions posed at the brief should give the technical author a very good idea of the scope of the intended manual and its contents, and provide him with ideas as to its presentation.

BREAKDOWN OF THE MANUAL

Irrespective of the complexity of a manual, the titles of its main headings (or topics) will generally be the same. These titles are shown in Figure 3.1, and are what the reader will look for in his rapid search for information.

Depending on the size of the manual, these titles assume a graded or hierarchical order. For instance, each one of the titles shown in Figure 3.1 may be the subject of a volume, a section, a chapter, or (for a small content manual) a centre heading. If the title is the subject of a volume, then that volume will also include a contents list of the sections and/or chapters it contains. In a similar manner each section will have a contents list of the chapters it contains, and each chapter will have a contents list of its own contents.

It is worth mentioning at this point that, when a manual comprises more than one volume, the contents page for any *one* of the volumes should include the contents of *all* the volumes (*see* Figure 3.2). This practice greatly speeds the reader's search for information, since he doesn't have to look at each volume in turn and scan its contents for what he wants.

DATA (or Leading Particulars)
INTRODUCTION
INSTALLATION (if applicable)
OPERATING INSTRUCTIONS
DESCRIPTION
MAINTENANCE (or Overhaul)
FAULT FINDING
PARTS LISTS

Fig. 3.1   Typical contents breakdown.

Let us assume that the equipment being described is sufficiently large to warrant a three-volume manual divided as follows:

Volume 1   Setting to Work and Operation
Volume 2   Description
Volume 3   Maintenance and Repair

A typical contents page, included in each of the three volumes, is shown in Figure 3.2. From it we can see that, if the reader is interested only in the maintenance of say, Unit D, he will quickly discover that the required information is in Volume 3, Chapter 6, irrespective of which volume first comes to hand. Having been directed to Volume 3, Chapter 6, the reader will then scan the contents page of that chapter to discover a particular area of information. A typical contents list for the said Chapter 6 is shown in Figure 3.3.

VOLUME 1 – SETTING-TO-WORK & OPERATION

CONTENTS

VOLUME 2 – DESCRIPTION

CONTENTS

VOLUME 3 – MAINTENANCE & REPAIR

CONTENTS

Fig. 3.2   Typical contents page for a volume in a multi-volume manual.

CHAPTER 6

UNIT D

CONTENTS

Fig. 3.3   Typical contents page for a chapter.

'Contents of the Contents'   The following gives a general guide to the sort of information the reader will expect to find against each of the titles for the typical contents breakdown shown in Figure 3.1:

Data   Sometimes referred to as 'leading particulars', this part of the manual may not warrant its own volume, section, or chapter but will be inserted at the front of the manual in the form of preliminary pages. Its purpose is to provide quick answers for readers who are familiar with the equipment covered by the manual, or who already possess equipment of a similar nature and wish to discover the operational differences. The information provided is sub-divided under headings of *Mechanical* and *Electrical*, and includes dimensions, weights, operating temperatures, capacities of all storage tanks (fuel, oil, water, etc.), input and output voltage supply levels and current ratings, and all maximum and minimum operating conditions. The information will also include all operating pressures, types of oils to be used in specific places, shaft speeds and torques.

Introduction   This is probably the most difficult part of the manual to compose since it must be aimed to inform without over-informing and saturating the reader. Only main items of the equipment should be dealt with, and the theme of the text should be 'What is the purpose of the equipment?' and 'What are the components of the equipment allowing it to perform its purpose?' To give the optimum level of information under this heading requires a firm understanding (or 'feel') of the equipment concerned, and an experienced writer will normally leave this part of the manual until later in the writing project when he will inevitably have become conversant with all aspects of the equipment.

Installation   Many manuals deal with equipment already installed, and this topic will not normally be required. However, there are equipment and units which are crated and destined for installation in very confined spaces, in ships, aircraft and land vehicles. The purpose of this topic (if included) is to give the reader all the various dimensions of the equipment. The main dimensions will have been included in the data or leading particulars, but this part of the manual provides more specific information in the form of illustrations giving the centre-to-centre measurements of all fixing holes, radius of area required for opening hinged doors or panels, the recommended positions or points for lifting or hoisting, and so on. If a large unit is being dealt with, it is advisable to indicate its centre of gravity and (although probably mentioned elsewhere in the manual) to give its weight.

Operating instructions   This topic gives the reader precise instructions on how to operate the equipment, and procedures for dealing with emergencies. The instructions are given in a logical, sequential order, commencing with all the preliminary actions that must be performed and stating any prerequisites that must exist before operation can begin. (*See* also Health and Safety Instructions – page 48.)

Where a large system is involved, it is advisable to provide a table listing all the relevant controls and explaining the purpose of each. It is also important to bear in mind the location of the controls so that, if the sequence of operation permits, they can be operated and checked in groups. It is time-consuming – if not annoying – for an operator to be directed from one end of the equipment to the other, and then back to where he started.

The instructions must be laid out clearly and unambiguously, using the imperative mood (do this; check that). Also, use terminology that enables the operator to appreciate the function of a control so that he can better understand what he is doing; 'Set the power selector switch S1 to 115V 60 Hz' is more informative than 'Set S1 to 115V 60 Hz'.

Whether the equipment is as simple as a vacuum cleaner or as complex as a manned spaceflight-centre control console, an illustration must be included to show the location of all switches, controls, indicator lamps, etc. The exact wording used on the function labels must also be used in the written instructions and set in capitals, e.g. 'Set POWER switch to ON position and check that the adjacent red PWR ON indicator lamp lights'. The combination of illustrations, precise terminology and clear, well-presented instructions serve to reassure the operator that what he is doing is correct and will not damage the equipment.

Finally, the operating instructions must be proved. Whenever possible, this proving exercise should be undertaken by a person who is unfamiliar with the equipment being operated and who has not previously seen the operating instructions. If the instructions are good, the guinea-pig operator should have no problems; if he stumbles in any way, the writer must take note and amend his text accordingly.

Description   For this topic, the technical author has to work really hard: as an engineer who has to assess all the retrieved information and separate the wheat from the chaff, and as the writer who is presenting the information. From the writing point of view, he must set out his description in a logical presentation using no difficult words; no ambiguous words or terms; not giving too much detail nor yet too little. He must make full use of informative illustrations such as flow charts, circuit diagrams and any other type of drawing which will assist the description and help the reader.

The reader must be 'led by the hand' from the beginning of the chapter, through the middle and to its conclusion. The exposition of a description has been defined as: 'First you tell your reader what you are going to tell him, then you tell him and then you tell him what you've told him – a neat summary of the importance of exposition in terms of cohesion, liaison and interweaving the individual sentences and paragraphs making the whole.

If the description is for a system, maintain a system 'tempo' in the exposition. If the description is for a unit or component within the system, keep the exposition within the confines of that unit or component. If this discipline is not rigidly observed, the poor reader (new to the equipment and to the manual) will become completely confused.

As stated in Chapter 10, it is necessary at times to differentiate between the overall description of the equipment or system and the detailed description of components which would be required only by maintenance staff involved in overhauling the components. The latter type of descriptive material may be better placed as an introduction to the associated maintenance instructions.

From the engineering viewpoint, the author must *know* his subject (and the equipment in particular) so that his writing is not naïve but will give hard-fact information, confidence and interest to the reader. For example, little confidence would be imparted by a manual on aviation practice if the writer made such statements as 'The driver of the aeroplane must ensure that the fan at the front of the 'plane is clear before cranking the motor'.

Maintenance   This topic must start with paragraphs which define the maintenance philosophy for the equipment. For instance, to what level it will be disassembled, which items will be serviced or repaired, and which items will be repaired by replacement only. When applicable, detailed component descriptions should precede the associated maintenance procedures.

Attention must be drawn to any special procedures, and a list given of any special tools or test equipment. Having established the basic maintenance requirements, the writer then proceeds to give step-by-step instructions on what to do in a sequence appropriate to the logical, mechanical breakdown of the equipment. The demand on the writer's skill in exposition and syntax is not as exacting for this topic as it is for the introduction or the description. Exposition of the topic is already dictated by the sequence of things to be done, and the instructions are necessarily confined to imperative statements similar to those in the operating instructions.

Illustrations are essential for this topic if each instruction is to be kept brief. Moreover, the illustrations should carry indirect (numbered) annotations against the items pointed out so that in the instructions these numbers can be given instead of protracted nomenclature. But note that when an illustration bears indirect annotations, the text must carry a key to identify the various items.

The maintainer must always be in the writer's mind. The instructions given will be more appreciated if fewer words are used for stating the obvious, and more words are used where the maintainer needs to be reminded of certain points or cautioned when there might be risk of hazard to the equipment or himself.

Fault finding   If a description has been well written, one might think that the reader could perform his own fault finding based on the sound knowledge he had gained, and this would be correct – but only if the reader had read and fully appreciated the description. Remember the statements at the beginning of this chapter, and the 'roulette' chance of which pages will or will not be read. Fault finding is a vital topic if the reader is to retrieve information quickly and if equipment 'downtime' is to be minimized.

The fault-finding topic requires little writing effort, but it does call for ingenuity in presenting easy-to-follow fault tables or diagrams giving the reasons for a fault and the appropriate remedies. If these tables are to be properly organized, the author must clearly understand the building blocks and 'event' chains which enable the equipment to function. He will then carefully weigh all the *possible* faults that could occur and balance them against the servicing philosophy defined in the maintenance topic. (After all, if the maintenance philosophy is one of repair-by-replacement, then no fault finding is necessary – end of topic!)

If there is no maintenance/servicing philosophy, the author must establish in his own mind the limits to which he will take the fault-finding sequence; an unwary author could easily find himself ensnared in a 'fault progression' saga in which a fault will be attributed to just about everything possible. While this can be true of a fault, a boundary must be drawn somewhere in the interests of equipment-user confidence and economics.

When organizing the fault-finding topic, always list the possible faults that could occur in a sequence starting with the worst event (for example, 'Transmitter fails to transmit'), and finishing with the least important event (for example, 'Transmitter indicator lamp fails to light'). In the same way, always list the possible causes for each fault in a sequence starting with the simplest cause (for example, 'Supply fuse FS1 ruptured') and finishing with the more complex cause (for example, 'Open circuit output stage on PCB3').

Parts lists   This topic contains the part numbers, or other identifying numbers, of recommended spares for the equipment. Alternatively, the parts lists may have to show a complete breakdown of the equipment. The parts are listed hierarchically: main unit, sub-assemblies and components associated with each sub-assembly. Each part listed will usually have been shown in an illustration contained somewhere in the manual – certainly in the description and maintenance topics. Where the parts lists topic is the subject of a self-contained volume, it will generally become an illustrated parts catalogue (IPC) containing illustrations specially prepared for parts list identification. It is worth noting that, when this is the case, some of these illustrations should be used to assist the maintenance topic; they are very well drawn, and will certainly help to reduce the cost of preparing that topic.

Because these illustrations are expensive to prepare, use of a comprehensive parts list such as an IPC must be justified by the dictates of the handbook specification, or by the client's requirements or a contractual requirement of long-term spares back-up.

Appendixes   Before concluding these statements on general contents breakdown, it must be stressed that, during the course of actually preparing a manual, there are bound to arise certain subjects which do not fit into the already established breakdown. These subjects can be incorporated into the manual without disturbing its breakdown by including the information as an appendix (or a series of appendixes) inserted either at the back of the manual or at the end of the appropriate topic(s).

HEALTH AND SAFETY INSTRUCTIONS

Every manual must include the instructions and information necessary to ensure the safe use of the equipment, and in many countries there are legal requirements to this effect. Safety instructions can be divided into three basic types:

- General descriptive explanations which provide an informative background to the specific warnings and instructions.
- Warnings of specific dangers.
- Precise instructions which must be followed to avoid the dangers.

A fundamental rule is that every warning or precautionary instruction must be accompanied by an explanation. A reader of a safety warning should never be left wondering why he has been given the warning; this would tempt him to disobey the warning.

In Britain, the Health and Safety at Work Act, 1974 lays down certain requirements relating to the provisions of safety instructions and warnings, and failure to comply can constitute an offence. Guidance Note GS 8 issued by the Health and Safety Commission, from which the following quotations were taken, gives guidance on the applications of the Act. Although prosecutions under the Act can apply to individual employees, this is unlikely unless 'the evidence indicated that he had not simply made a mistake but had acted wilfully, knowing that he was in breach of the law'.

The duties imposed by the Act include the following which are especially relevant to technical publications:

> 'to ensure, so far as is reasonably practicable', that articles and substances for use at work are 'safe and without risk to health when properly used'.

> to ensure 'that there will be available in connection with the use of the article at work adequate information about the use for which it is designed and has been tested and about any conditions necessary to ensure' safety and absence of risks to health when put to that use.

The term 'when properly used' presumes that people will behave in a way that can reasonably be expected. And if the user makes an unusual or unexpected use of the equipment or disregards the information supplied, this will not be regarded as proper use.

In relation to 'proper use', it is important to specify in the manual the use for which the equipment was designed and tested and to list all limitations affecting the operation of the equipment, for example, critical maximum and minimum pressures and temperatures. Usually it is convenient to do this in the data section and then to make reference to the data section at other appropriate places.

In the framing of instructions and warnings, it is essential to take into account the technical and linguistic abilities of people who could reasonably be expected to use the equipment. At times this could entail providing instructions in more than one language; on other occasions it would be reasonable to presume a high degree of technical training – for example, the operating instructions for an airliner's navigational equipment. It is not necessary to spell out hazards that are completely obvious. Clearly, nearly every article is potentially dangerous if dropped from a great height; so there is no need to warn against this.

There is an implicit commitment in the Act to keep information up to date. If research after the equipment has gone into service brings to light new information that could affect the safety of the equipment, then there is a duty under the Act to pass this information on to the user.

When, as often happens, safety instructions written by a technical author are vetted by an engineer, scientist or manager, the act of vetting does not necessarily absolve the author from his own obligations to take reasonable steps to ascertain possible hazards and provide the necessary safety warnings and instructions.

PRESENTATION OF THE MANUAL

Apart from any aesthetic appeal, the finished manual's presentation must be such that the reader can quickly find information which, when found, can then be clearly read. And because technical manuals frequently have to be amended to keep pace with design changes in the equipment they support, the presentation must lend itself to easy amendment.

The handbook specification will invariably detail the presentation to be adopted. Indeed, except for minor variations, all specifications have very similar requirements in this respect. In the absence of any such specification, the technical author should adopt the best features of presentation from all the specifications known to him.

Presentation Requirements   The following section lists and describes the basic requirements of presentation:

Type of paper   Paper is specified by its weight (g.s.m.) and is always white unless otherwise specified. Generally, paper weight governs its transparency; the grade chosen is that at which there is just no 'show-through'. Minimal 'show-through' is important because, in order to reduce weight and bulk, a manual has each leaf printed on both sides.

Another factor which will determine the choice of paper is the type of book. Thus, a workshop manual which will be in constant use may well need to be printed on a heavier paper. Also, because of the environment in which it will be used, the paper may be encapsulated or plasticized so that it can be wiped clean of oily finger marks.

Page size   As mentioned earlier, the page size of the finished manual must be determined very early so that its content can be estimated. The page size used will dictate the text area per page, once the binding margin, fore-edge margin and top and bottom margins have been incorporated.

Margins   Nearly all manuals are loose-leaf and bound in a ring-binder cover. This requires the pages to be hole-punched along the binding margin, and the diameter of these holes can vary. The dimension of the binding margin must therefore be sufficient to accommodate the type of binding used without obscuring the text. The dimension of the fore-edge margin, that is the margin opposite the binding margin, is not critical but should be wide enough so as not to allow any line of text to 'bleed' off the page.

The dimensions of the top and bottom margins also are not critical but they should be sufficiently deep to allow for such information as the publication, chapter, and page identification (*see* Figure 3.4).

Type face   It can be difficult in these days of word processors and high-quality electronic typewriters (both fixed-pitch and proportional spacing) to insist that any particular type face be used. The chief requirements are that it be clear, consistent and (most important) that it lends itself to being matched at a future date should amendments or revisions to the text be required.

Some specifications recommend a large type face (for example, pica rather than elite) for maintenance or workshop manuals, which may have to be read under difficult conditions.

Paragraphs   To facilitate quick reference, and for assisting amendment action, each paragraph is sequentially numbered. Adequate space is given between the paragraph number and the start of the opening sentence, and some specifications emphasize this by incorporating a double indentation.

An extra space is also included between paragraphs, between paragraphs and sub-paragraphs and between paragraphs (or sub-paragraphs) and a note, caution or warning.

Notes, cautions and warnings   When these are used in the body of a text (as distinct from being the subject of a preliminary page), they are not

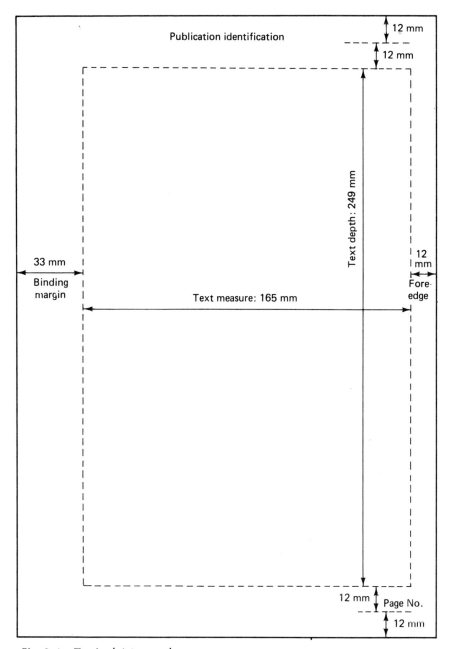

Fig. 3.4 Typical A4-page layout.
The dimensions shown are for a right-hand (recto) page. A
left-hand (verso) page is a mirror image of this layout.

accorded a paragraph number but are treated as entities. Each is given its own style of presentation so as to emphasize its importance. (*See* also Health and Safety Instructions – page 48.)

The definitions of a note, caution and warning are as follows:

A *note* furnishes additional information to assist the reader when reading a particular paragraph.

A *caution* provides the reader with advice which, if disregarded, could cause damage to the equipment.

A *warning* gives the reader information (or a command) which, if disregarded, could cause injury or death. Because of its importance, any warning must precede the instruction(s) which, in the act of being performed, could be dangerous.

Contents page   The contents page must direct the reader to a particular paragraph or page on which he will find exactly the information he is looking for. Figure 3.3 shows a typical contents page presentation. The wording of each heading – as well as the wording of each table and illustration title – must be the same as the wording to which it refers in the text, table or illustration. Note that the eye is led from the heading to the particular paragraph number by a series of leader dots. Many specifications omit these from their examples of presentation. If so, it is sensible to question this omission; it is very irritating for the reader to discover that he hasn't arrived at the information he is seeking because of a crossover while his eyes were scanning from left to right of the contents page.

Illustrations   The comments made for text margins also apply to illustrations; for text area read illustration area. For illustrations which are to be set within the body of the text (insets), the width of the illustration area should not exceed the text measure. Note that all annotations also form part of the illustration area, but that the title does not. Thus, while the text area for a full-page or a fold-out page will also apply to an illustration, the depth dimension must be reduced slightly to allow for the figure number and title.

Consistency of annotation sizes and line thickness (where line drawings are concerned) is also desirable for the presentation of the manual.

Typing   Very few manuals are set by a printer from draft copy provided. Instead, the printer uses typed 'camera-ready' copy supplied by the technical author. The typist involved therefore makes a major contribution to the manual's presentation, and the technical author soon discovers in his career that the typist is a valuable colleague. From the time that the first draft chapters are being typed until the camera copy is being prepared, the typist will be following – if not implementing – the required page presentation.

The typist's skill ensures that page after page leaves the typewriter as though jig-set – well-fitted words within the text measure; well-set lines within the text depth; page numbers all set in exactly the same place; consistent spacing between paragraphs and sub-paragraphs; no characters overtyped nor any obvious corrections. The sum of all these points, and the effort applied by the technical author to shape and fill the contents, will result in a well-prepared manual and a satisfied reader. Always remember the reader.

CHAPTER 4

Illustrations for Technical Publications

by
Larry Irvin

INTRODUCTION

In any publication conveying information, the illustration, or the visual representation of the subject matter is a vital partner to the text: one should support the other.

Communicating by pictures goes back to primitive man and, of course, the written word itself has its origins in hieroglyphics and symbols used for this purpose. When one considers how easily and quickly a message can be communicated pictorially without the problem of the language barrier, it is easy to understand the importance of the role of the illustrator – or graphic interpreter of the message. Colour too is a visual form of communication which can be used in many ways, such as signals or coding, as a universal language.

This should not be taken to mean that the illustration is more important than the text. Visual communication of information in partnership with the text is the true function of a scientific or technical illustration.

An illustration should be precise and without ambiguity, for example, substituting symbols for the words MEN and WOMEN on a public convenience is pointless if it is impossible to determine which symbol is the man and which is the woman.

A visually communicated message can range from a simple arrow indicating direction, to a highly detailed colour drawing or photograph showing every detail of the subject; but each is as important as the other if skilfully chosen for its particular function.

The basis of the subject matter may be medical or biological; architectural or scientific; or as the samples used in this book, manufacturing and engineering. The approach, however, to choosing the correct illustration should always be the same.

The first consideration of any illustration should be: What is its purpose? What job must it do? At the same time the end-user or reader should be taken into account. In other words: What is likely to be his level of technical skill or knowledge of the subject?

The other main factor for consideration is: How or in what form is the illustration to be reproduced? There may be a few occasions when an illustration is used in its original form, such as in an exhibition or display of some kind, but the bulk of the illustrator's work is producing illustrations for publication, and his skills should include a good working knowledge of the process of graphic reproduction and printing.

Finally, when planning a series of illustrations for a publication, cost and time must be taken into account. The possibility of using an illustration in more than one place should be examined. Sometimes an illustration can be prepared with two clear overlays, one with the items numbered for use with the parts list, and the other with annotations for descriptive and maintenance material. Manufacturer's orthographic (*see* page 61) production drawings can often be converted into perfectly adequate sectional illustrations at quite a considerable saving of time and cost. Photographs can sometimes be used, but although often pleasing to look at and in the case of promotional material assuring the customer of the existence of the product (not always the case, however), they do have certain limitations. First, it may not be possible to set up the equipment exactly as required for the purpose of the illustration. Second, the detail required may be at an angle or in a position that the camera cannot reach. This in turn may mean that further work by the illustrator may be required before the picture can be used. In any case there will almost always need to be some form of retouching or preparation before the photograph can be processed for reproduction. Another consideration is that photographs do not reproduce so well as line drawings on copying machines, and can therefore present duplicating problems for any material in which they are included.

All these factors should be taken into account at the earliest planning stages of any publication so that coverage of the subject matter can be the most efficient and effective in every aspect.

TYPES OF ILLUSTRATION

Making the Choice   At the earliest possible stage in the production of any sort of publication, consideration must be made by all concerned as to what form the illustrations are to take. Since the cost of the illustrations is a major factor in the overall cost of a publication, it is advisable that the graphic department is represented from the first day of planning.

Many of the early questions to be asked about the illustrations will be the same as for the text (*see* Chapters 2, 3 and 10) and close liaison between author and illustrator will result in valuable saving of cost and time.

Where a standard specification for the book is to be followed then many of the basic questions will be resolved. However, it may be that no fixed format has been considered, or perhaps a feasibility study is to be made to decide just what the budget will allow.

Unless the publication is to be a prestigious, spare-no-expense project, the most important factor for consideration is cost. It would be ideal if each illustration in a book could be considered on its own merits, and in some cases this may be so, but as most engineering publications contain several sections such as description, operation and maintenance, the same illustration could be used more than once. It may even be possible, where the equipment to be illustrated is suitable, to use the same base illustration throughout a whole series (*see* the section 'Planning a Series' of illustrations) in which case cost will be reduced and efficiency improved.

Photographs or drawings? There are many pros and cons to be considered when weighing the merits of photographs against drawings. If a good photograph of the subject exists and covers the details required, then it may be considered. But, take into account the cost of preparing it as a half-tone illustration and whether the equipment is likely to be changed in any way, making modifications necessary; very often this occurs just before publication. It may be possible to convert a photograph to a line drawing quite simply by tracing off an enlarged print. If photographs are to be taken, then consider the following:

When will the equipment be at the build stage required? Every item needed to be seen should be fitted when the photograph is taken, and the equipment cleared of anything that may confuse the reader, such as test gauges, wires, fitter's tools and tea mugs, etc. This will avoid expensive retouching by the artist.

Can the equipment be placed in a suitable position for the photograph? It must be possible to light the subject adequately, and arrange the camera at a suitable angle for the photograph.

How long will the equipment be available? Remember it takes time to set up a photographic session, and fitters on a production bonus will not be very sympathetic if they are held up for too long. Also, if the equipment is ready for delivery to the customer, the financial department will be quite anxious to see it on its way.

If all these questions can be answered satisfactorily, then photographs may be suitable, otherwise line drawings will be the answer.

Line Drawings
The term 'line drawing' refers to any drawing or illustration that consists simply of black lines on a white background, or the reverse. In other words, every mark and the paper or material on which it is made has a black to white contrast, without variation in tone as in a photograph, airbrush, pencil or wash drawing (*see* the section 'Continuous Tone').

In a line illustration, the form or shape of the subject, surface textures or tonal variations must all be indicated by a black line or dot (*see* the section 'Techniques and Equipment') but within these limits there is scope for a wide variation of choice. One of the main advantages of the line drawing is that it can be easily reproduced, by direct copying methods, printing or, if on a translucent background, by dyeline printing. There are many categories of line drawings as will be seen in the following paragraphs, and the most suitable for all the purposes required should be chosen.

System Diagrams
If an engineering manual covers one or more electrical, pneumatic, hydraulic or similar system, then usually the most important pages in the book will be the system diagrams. These will be the pages that will be consulted first in the event of a problem. Well laid out, comprehensively annotated, system diagrams tell an engineer a lot about how the system works, how it should be operated and what faults are likely. It is therefore essential that a great deal of thought and care are directed towards achieving the highest possible standard of system diagrams.

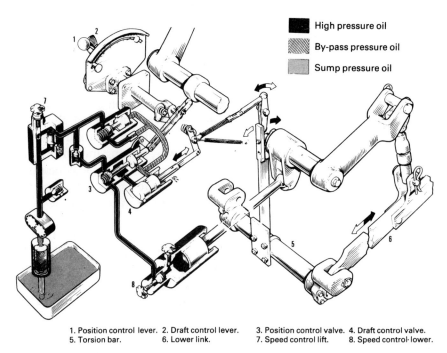

High pressure oil

By-pass pressure oil

Sump pressure oil

1. Position control lever. 2. Draft control lever. 3. Position control valve. 4. Draft control valve.
5. Torsion bar. 6. Lower link. 7. Speed control lift. 8. Speed control· lower.

Fig. 4.1   Pictorial functional diagram.

The prime responsibility for determining the form and content of system diagrams must rest with the author. Nevertheless, a good illustrator working in close co-operation with an author can be more than just an embellisher of the author's rough layout. If the illustrator follows the logic of the layout, he may be able to spot errors or omissions, or be able to suggest improvements to the layout.

There are four main forms of system diagrams: (*a*) pictorial functional

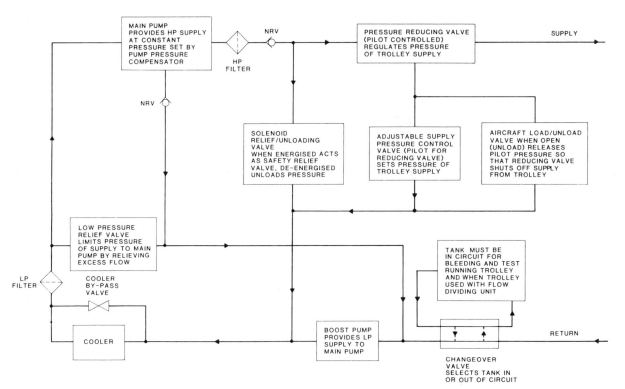

Fig. 4.2   Block diagram with layout to match circuit diagram.

diagrams; (*b*) block functional diagrams; (*c*) theoretical circuit diagrams; and (*d*) physical system diagrams showing the physical locations of components and their interconnecting wiring and piping. The four types of diagram perform different functions, and unless the system is very simple, it is best not to try to combine more than one function on one diagram – for example, by endeavouring to show the physical layout on a theoretical circuit.

Pictorial functional diagrams (see Figure 4.1) The purpose of this type of diagram is to give the reader an overall view of the system and the functional relationship of its main units. The diagram shows the approximate physical positions of the main units in the system and how they function. Annotations, explanatory notes, flow arrows and similar devices can be used to explain the method of functioning, but unless the system is simple the explanation will be in only very broad terms.

Functional block diagrams (see Figure 4.2) This type of diagram uses blocks of text laid out in a logical sequence to explain, in broad terms, the functional relationships of the main units in the system. Block diagrams are also used to show the interfaces between various sub-systems of the complete equipment, for example, between a hydraulic system and its associated electrical control circuit.

No attempt is made to show the relative physical positions of the system's components. However, sometimes it is possible to lay out a block diagram so that it approximately corresponds to the layout of the associated theoretical circuit (*see* Figures 4.2 and 4.3); this is very helpful to the reader. Even better is to place the block diagram and theoretical circuit on facing pages, so that the reader can readily read across from one to the other.

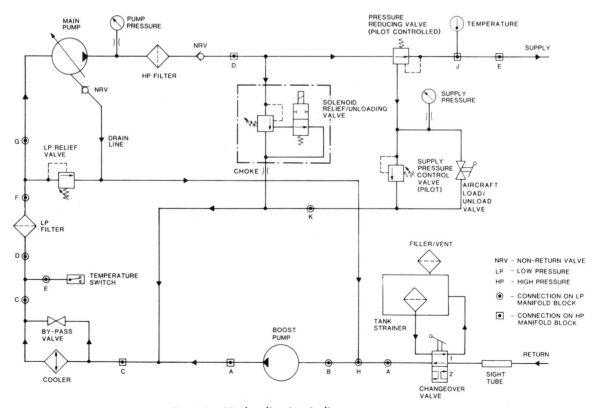

Fig. 4.3 Hydraulic circuit diagram.

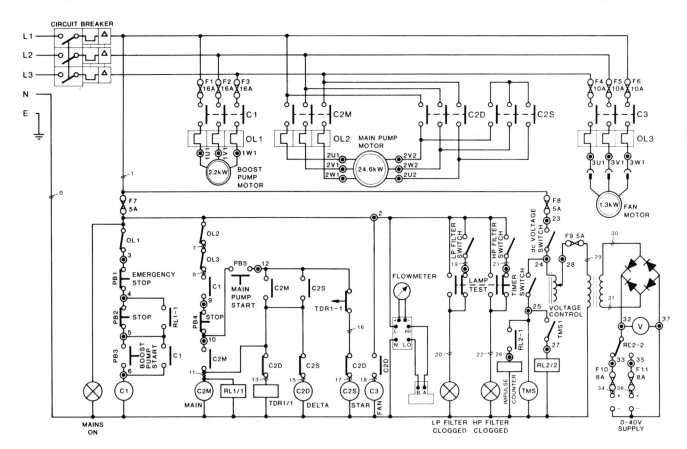

Fig. 4.4   Theoretical circuit diagram – electrical.

Theoretical circuit diagrams (see Figures 4.3 and 4.4)   The theoretical circuit shows the functional relationship of every item in the system, though not necessarily all on one sheet. Complex circuits may comprise many interrelated sheets, and cross reference may be made to another document for a section of the circuit. When the complete circuit is shown on several sheets, the first sheet should be an overall diagram showing how all the subsequent sheets are interrelated.

Usually it is not beneficial to attempt to show the physical relationships on a theoretical circuit; this only confuses the issue.

Electrical circuits are now normally drawn using the separated-contacts method, by which the operating coil of a relay or similar device is not positioned on the circuit adjacent to the contacts that it operates. The circuit positions of the coil and contacts are determined solely by functional relationships. Circuits drawn on an entirely functional basis in this way greatly facilitate understanding of the system and fault diagnosis. Figure 4.5 shows a simple example of a car starting circuit drawn (*a*) using a physical layout and (*b*) using the modern, functional, separated-contacts method.

The key factors in laying out a theoretical circuit are that all main supply lines and flow paths should be straight, and that crossing lines should be reduced to the absolute minimum. This will enable the reader to rapidly comprehend the predominant functional relationships, because his eye will automatically follow the main straight lines of function. The normal convention is for the main sequences or flow paths to go from left to right across the page, as this is the natural direction of reading.

Often, it is not easy to achieve the optimum layout, and if the system is

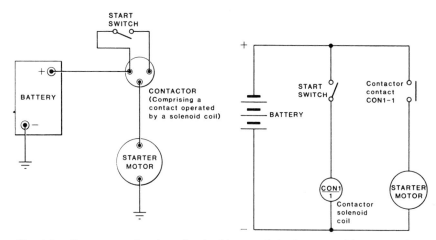

Fig. 4.5   Car starter circuit – physical layout (left), functional layout (right).

complex several attempts and a lot of trial and error will be involved. However, the time spent in achieving a good circuit is time well spent.

Care should be taken that terminology used on a theoretical circuit diagram corresponds with that used elsewhere. For example, if a solenoid valve is called SOL 2 on a pneumatic circuit, it causes chaos to annotate it SOL 3 on the electrical circuit.

The information content and ease of understanding of a theoretical circuit is greatly enhanced by comprehensive annotations and brief explanatory notes. Even when British Standard circuit symbols are used, it is usually preferable to annotate each component; although if the same component is used at a number of locations one annotation will probably suffice.

Physical system diagrams (see Figure 4.6)   These diagrams are designed to convey *physical* as distinct from *functional* information. Their purpose is to show where the particular components of a system are located and how they are connected to other components.

For electrical equipment this will normally involve a wiring diagram showing the locations of the components and all the cable and terminal numbers. There are various forms of interconnection diagrams which can also be used. When the complete diagram comprises several sheets, the first sheet should show how all the subsequent sheets correlate.

Whenever practicable, piping diagrams should be drawn in perspective, especially if some of the readers may have limited technical knowledge. A less time-consuming but graphically inferior alternative is a two dimensional line diagram on which the main components are shown located in their approximate relative positions.

Colour   Most diagrams can be made clearer by the use of colour, especially those showing flow paths of gases, fluids, etc., but of course this means that production costs for the publication will be increased. If this is not possible then tonal effects could be used to differentiate between areas on the diagram, and there is a wide range of mechanical tints that can be used for this purpose (*see* the section 'Techniques and Equipment').

Charts and Graphs   Graphical representation of statistical information is constantly being used, and examples such as political trends, rise and fall of inflation, how

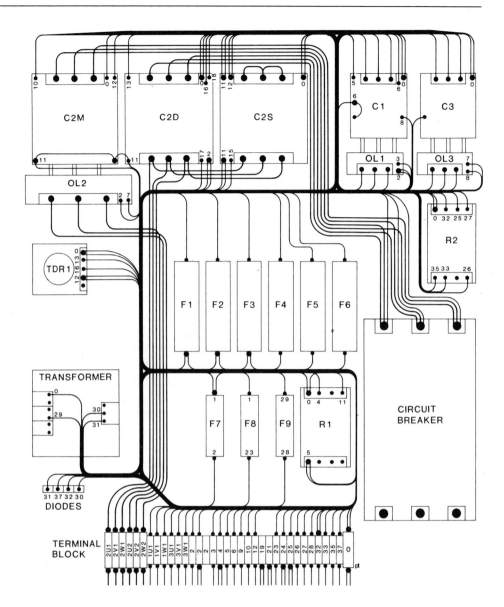

Fig. 4.6   Physical wiring diagram.

government expenditure is apportioned, etc., can be seen almost daily in one form or another. A well thought out graph or chart can instantly convey the relevance of facts or figures that may otherwise be tedious and difficult to follow.

This type of information can be divided into three categories: trends and movements; percentages and quantities; and comparisons.

Graphs   Trends or movements such as sales figures, temperatures, etc., can usually be best shown as a line on a graph.

Graphs for publication should be as simple as possible, depending on how precise the information has to be. If a grid is used the lines should be kept to a minimum and preferably be a different colour, but this of course depends on the budget for the publication.

Pie and bar charts   Percentages and quantities can best be represented by pie or bar charts. A pie chart is a circle – or pie – divided into segments to illustrate portions of a whole. For instance, if the whole pie represents 100%, then 25% would be represented by a quarter segment. The bar chart shows quantities or divisions of amounts by bars of varying lengths (*see* Figure 4.7).

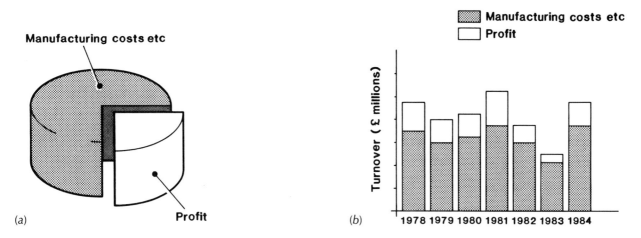

Fig. 4.7   (a) Pie chart.   (b) Bar chart.

Column charts   Comparative quantities or groups are best shown by column charts, in which amounts and quantities can be compared to each other by the varying heights of columns. Similar comparisons can be made for masses which can also be represented by symbols. For example, bags of money, barrels of oil, groups of people, etc. (*see* Figure 4.8).

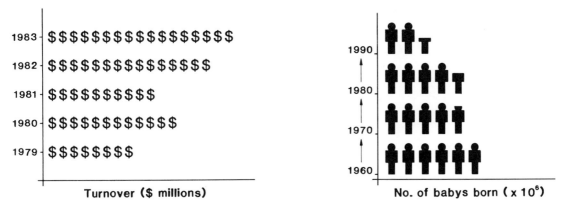

Fig. 4.8   Column charts.

Simplicity and clarity should be the aim when drawing graphs and charts, and there are many graphical aids available today to help put over the message with the greatest possible effect.

Orthographic Drawing   An orthographic drawing may often be the most suitable way of illustrating the subject, and because in most cases it can be taken directly from the manufacturer's production drawing, it can be very cost effective. It still, however, has to be prepared by the illustrator for publication and to suit the requirements of the illustration.

The main limitation of orthographic drawing is that it is only a two dimensional or flat view on one side or plane of an object and therefore only details on that side can be shown. This can be overcome by including a view from another direction, either complete or in part (scrap view), depending on what hidden details need to be shown. Alternatively, if the illustration has to show details on every side of an object a conventional three view general arrangement can be used. Such a drawing can also be used to convey overall dimensions for installation instruction or to show clearances, etc., for servicing manuals (*see* Figure 4.9).

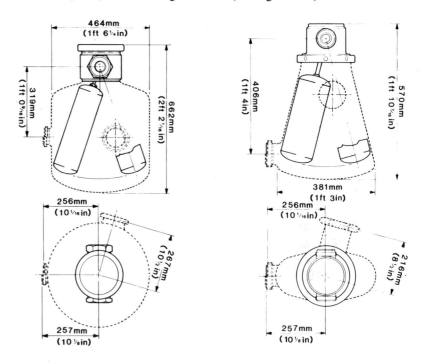

Fig. 4.9   Orthographic drawing showing overall dimensions.

Sectional view   Probably the most effective orthographic illustration is the sectional view, which shows the inner workings of the subject and can be used to show the principles of operation and flow paths as well as the locations of the working parts. It can be used to support descriptive and maintenance text, using direct annotations as in Figure 4.10, and again as a spare parts illustration using item numbers as in Figure 4.11. This can be achieved either by taking a secondary master from the original before annotating, or by using the original with two clear acetate overlays for the

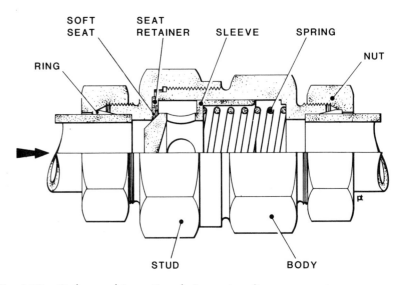

Fig. 4.10   Orthographic sectional view using direct annotations.

numbers and annotations. The latter means there is only one master to modify if there are any changes in the equipment. The disadvantage of a sectional view for a spare parts illustration is that the items are not isolated as in an exploded view (*see* Figure 4.15), but on the other hand it is generally easier to see the functional relationship between items on an assembly.

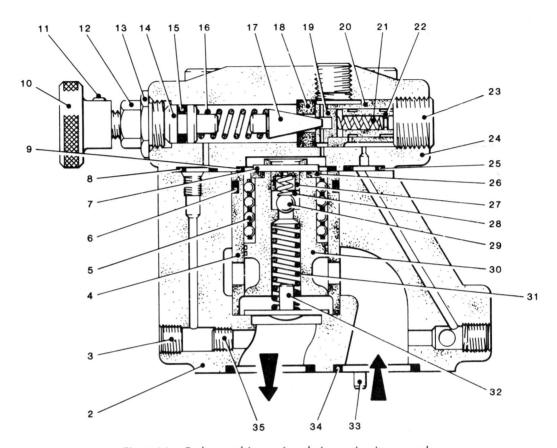

Fig. 4.11 Orthographic sectional view using item numbers.

The main advantage of an orthographic section is that it can cost only 25% of the figure for an equivalent perspective cutaway or exploded view, and generally the research involved is much less than for a perspective illustration. The reference material must be clear, however, and easy to follow. The magical powers that illustrators are supposed to possess that enable them to conjure up details out of the blue, under the heading of artistic licence, are very limited in a sectional view because of its functional nature, and a good copy of the original must be available.

The illustrator should prepare an orthographic view in a style consistent with that used throughout the publication and within the limits of interpretation by the end-user (*see* the section 'Reading Orthographic Drawings'), in other words he should make it an illustration for publication (*see* the section 'Techniques and Equipment').

Perspective Drawing The perspective illustration is the main part of the illustrator's craft. To plan and execute an illustration through all its stages, from initial construction to final inking is a very satisfying task, and the result can be fulfilling if not always financially rewarding. However, the cost and time involved must be justified.

Although in one or two cases the orthographic section has the advantage, the well planned perspective drawing has the ability to present a complete visual description of the subject. In one illustration it is possible to show the overall shape or profile of an object, plus inside details and inner workings (*see* Figure 4.12). This type of illustration uses several techniques, such as cutting away, ghosting and shading, and is particularly suitable for all promotional material such as press releases, brochures, tenders, etc., that need to give a complete picture.

Fig. 4.12   Promotional pictorial view.

External views   The external perspective is ideal for external views and locating external details, such as controls, fixings, gauges and access panels (*see* Figure 4.25). In cases where items are located on the unseen side of the object an inset detail can be included on the main illustration.

Cutaway views   The cutaway perspective is fundamentally a three dimensional sectional view. It is particularly suitable for subjects that are basically cylindrical or have a central axis, such as pumps, valves and filters, and the usual practice is to cut away a quarter segment to expose the inner details while still maintaining the external shape (*see* Figure 4.13). Of course, the technique can be applied to any subject, and the cutaway portion can be any shape or size, providing it is clearly presented and the object is still recognizable. As with the orthographic section, this type of illustration is particularly suitable for showing internal flow and principles of operation.

Exploded views   As the term implies, the exploded view (*see* Figure 4.14) has the appearance of an assembly having had its components blown out from the main body, but still remaining in relative order along their respective centrelines. This type of illustration can be used for a parts list (*see* Figure 4.15) where items need to be isolated from each other while still maintaining their sub-assembly groups. It is also ideal for showing the order of removal and assembly of components.

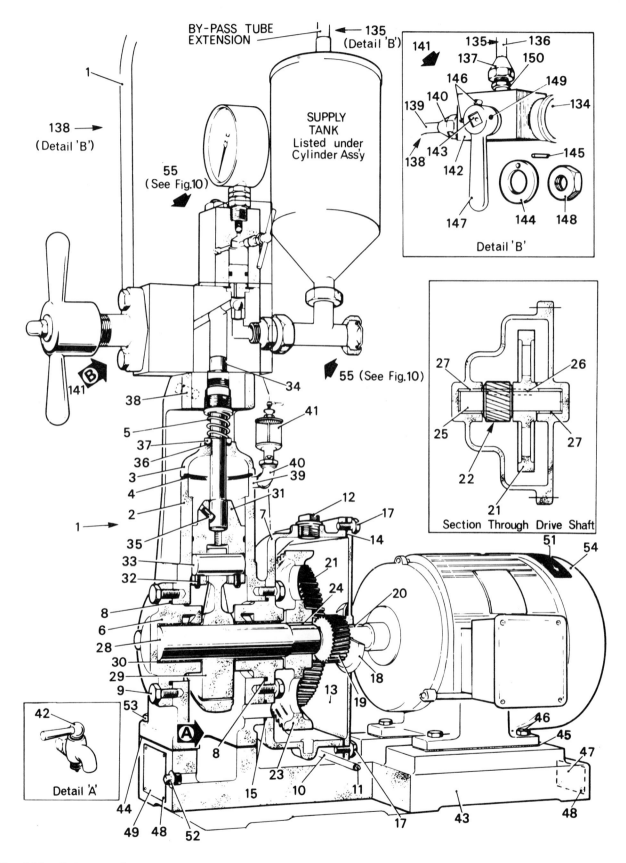

Fig. 4.13   Cut-away view.

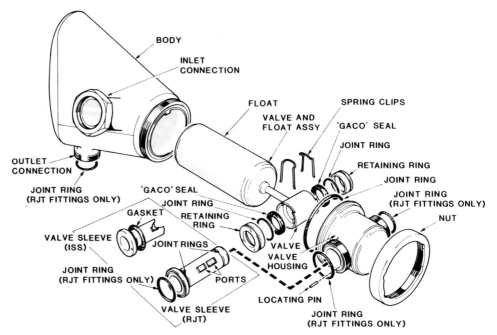

Fig. 4.14   Exploded view with direct annotations.

The exploded view can, however, present a problem of space if the subject is complex and has many items or if the main body fills the drawing area even before the items are pulled out. This can sometimes be overcome by staggering the centreline in a 'Z' formation, or by slightly overlapping each item, but not to the extent where they become unrecognizable. Care should also be taken not to make the drawing too fragmented so that it is impossible to see how the various sub-assemblies fit together.

One-point Perspective   One-point perspective is most suitable for viewing the interior of four-sided compartments like boxes or rooms. The vanishing point is at the centre of the picture which makes it possible to see the four surfaces at

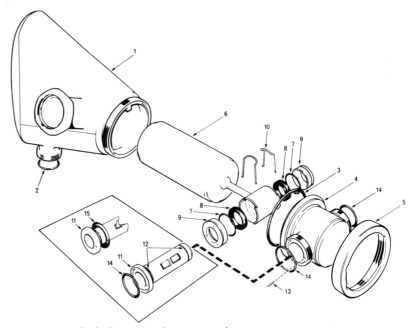

Fig. 4.15   Exploded view with item numbers.

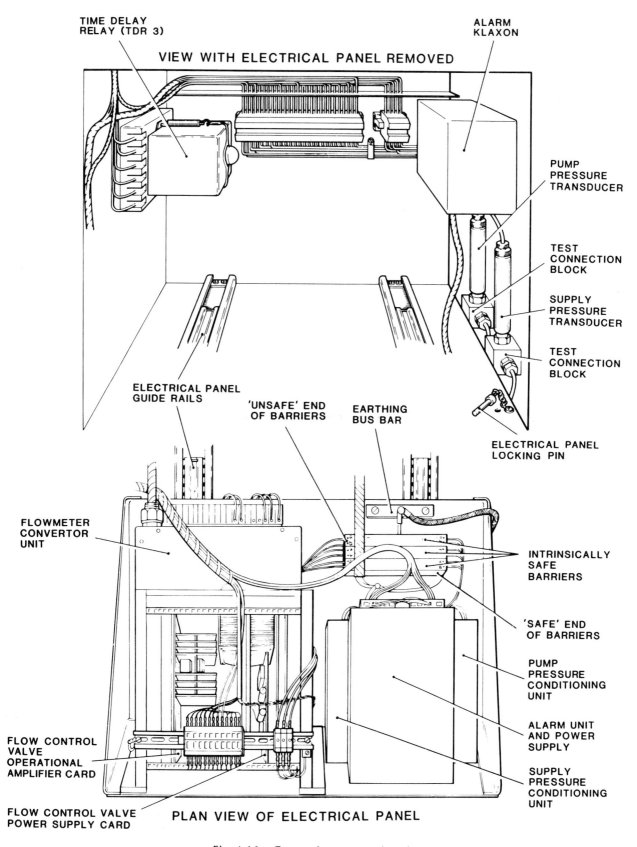

TIME DELAY
RELAY (TDR 3)

ALARM
KLAXON

VIEW WITH ELECTRICAL PANEL REMOVED

PUMP
PRESSURE
TRANSDUCER

TEST
CONNECTION
BLOCK

SUPPLY
PRESSURE
TRANSDUCER

TEST
CONNECTION
BLOCK

ELECTRICAL PANEL
GUIDE RAILS

'UNSAFE' END
OF BARRIERS

EARTHING
BUS BAR

ELECTRICAL PANEL
LOCKING PIN

FLOWMETER
CONVERTOR
UNIT

INTRINSICALLY
SAFE
BARRIERS

'SAFE' END
OF BARRIERS

PUMP
PRESSURE
CONDITIONING
UNIT

ALARM UNIT
AND POWER
SUPPLY

FLOW CONTROL
VALVE
OPERATIONAL
AMPLIFIER CARD

SUPPLY
PRESSURE
CONDITIONING
UNIT

FLOW CONTROL VALVE
POWER SUPPLY CARD

PLAN VIEW OF ELECTRICAL PANEL

Fig. 4.16   One-point perspective view.

once (*see* Figure 4.16). It is ideal for showing the layout of control rooms, control panels or components in a box or cabinet, but the degree of perspective is somewhat distorting.

Scenarios   There may be times when it will be necessary to illustrate the equipment in use. Here the ingenuity of the illustrator will be stretched to create a typical working environment for the subject, possibly including personnel (*see* Figure 4.17).

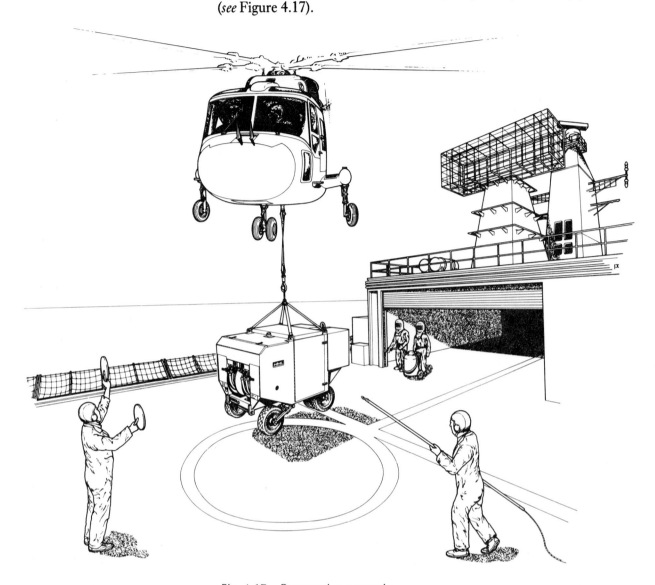

Fig. 4.17   Perspective scenario.

There are, however, many suitable techniques within the limits of line drawing that will enable him to make a satisfactory illustration at a fraction of the cost of setting up a photographic session, even if this were possible.

Continuous Tone   The difference between a photograph and a line drawing for publication is in the method of reproduction. On a line drawing the image is a black line on a white background or alternatively a white line on a black background, whereas on a photograph the image ranges from black to white through varying intensities of tonal values, or greys. This is called continuous tone and requires special processing for reproduction. It also applies to drawings that are not specifically black and white, but have tonal variations, such as wash drawings, pencil or charcoal drawings and drawings prepared with an airbrush. Artwork that comes into this category is referred to by the printer as half-tone.

To prepare a half-tone for printing it must be photographed through a very fine screen which breaks up the image into a series of tiny dots varying in density according to the different tonal values of the image (*see* Chapter 7). When it is printed each dot will print black on the paper in just the same way as the type matter or a line drawing, but because of the varying density of the dots it will appear to have tonal values similar to the photograph from which it was copied.

The categories of half-tone drawings are the same as for line drawings and any line drawing can be rendered in tone by painting or spraying with an airbrush to whatever effect is required. In this case the illustration will have to be treated as a photograph and screened for reproduction.

It is possible, however, to give a line drawing tonal or shaded effects by using mechanical tints (*see* the section 'Techniques and Equipment') but in this case the illustration still maintains its line characteristics, and screening for reproduction is not necessary.

A high-quality half-tone illustration can be very desirable for publicity and promotional material, and an expert airbrush artist can create a photographic impression of an object before it has been manufactured, but the cost is high and the original should be treated with the respect it merits.

Photographs   If all the points made at the beginning of this section about the use of photographs have been considered, the work necessary to prepare a photograph for publication will be reduced. There will, however, still be a certain amount of work to do depending on what the photograph has to show.

Retouching   Almost all photographs require a certain amount of retouching, but it should be the very minimum necessary. Some details may have to be strengthened and others removed. There may be blemishes or unwanted shadow or reflections on the picture that have to be taken out. The background may have to be altered, ghosted or completely taken out. All this is the work of the retouching artist, a highly skilled technician, using an airbrush (*see* the section 'Techniques and Equipment').

The airbrush   The airbrush is a small spray gun operated by compressed air. It is used to apply paint or ink in a very fine spray to match the tonal effects of a photograph. In this way a photograph can be altered or have detail added.

Two unglazed glossy prints should be supplied to the retoucher, and these should be handled with great care. Never write instructions on an overlay with a ball point pen or anything that might indent the surface of the picture, and never use paper clips, staples or anything that might scratch the surface in any way.

Cutaway half-tones   Figure 4.18 shows a photograph that has been cutaway to show interior details. Figure 4.19 shows a detail isolated from a larger photograph.

Squared-up half-tones   When a photograph or half-tone has the background left in, the border must be squared up to the picture size required for publication. The background detail can be lightened, 'ghosted' to emphasize a particular area, or it can be taken out completely and left a flat grey (*see* Figure 4.19).

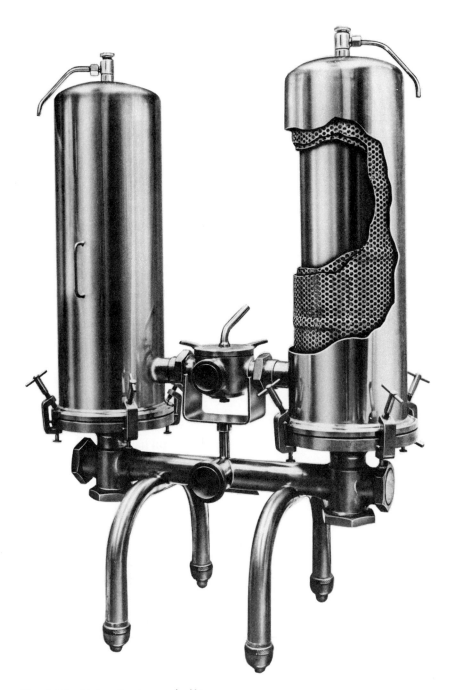

Fig. 4.18   Cut-out cutaway half-tone.

Cut-out half-tone   The background of a photograph or half-tone can be removed completely so that the object appears on a white background. This is called a cut-out half-tone (*see* Figure 4.20).

Annotations and leader lines   These can be either added directly to the photograph, in which case they will be half-tone screened with the photograph, or they can be put on a separate clear overlay. The latter is preferable as it allows for modification without affecting the photograph; also the annotations can either be screened with the photograph or treated as a line separation.

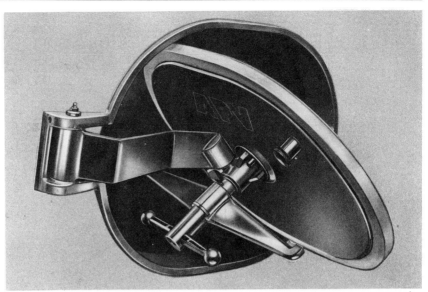

Fig. 4.19   *Squared-up half-tone detail.*

Fig. 4.20   *Cut-out half-tone – showing indication for removing background.*

Fig. 4.21   Airbrush drawing.

Fig. 4.22   Airbrush and wash scenario.

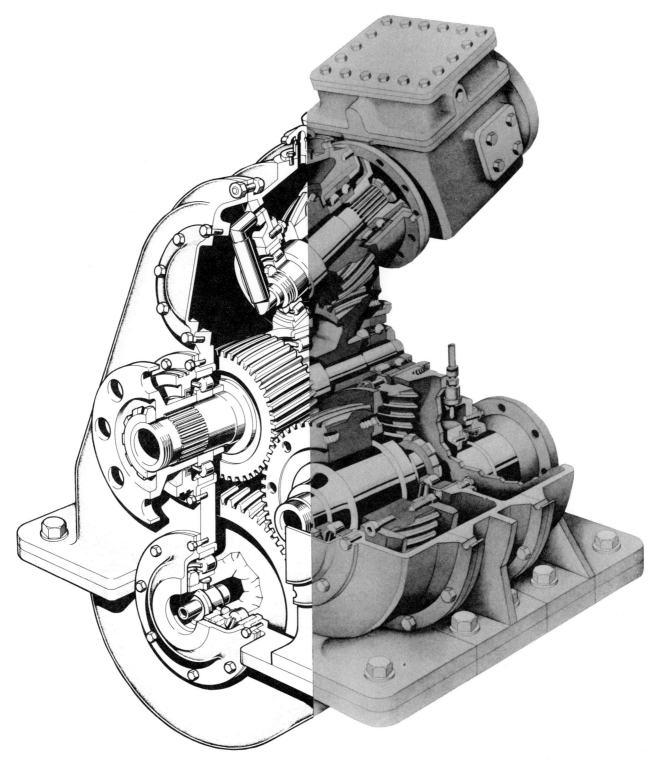

Fig. 4.23   *Gearbox demonstrating alternative line and wash treatments.*

Airbrush drawing   Just as it is possible to change detail on an actual photograph, a complete photographic picture can be created by the airbrush artist. Of course it is a very costly operation because of the work involved, but if the cost is justifiable it can be very effective.

The reasons for requiring a picture of this sort can be very varied. It may be that publicity pictures are needed for leaflets or a brochure for a trade fair, and the equipment has not yet been built, or it may be impossible to photograph from just the right angle.

A basic line drawing of the subject will have to be made first – if a line drawing exists it can be taken from this – and then a photographic copy of the line drawing made to whatever the size required. This can then be treated in the same way as a photograph for retouching (*see* Figure 4.21).

The airbrush can be used also to enhance the appearance of diagrams and line drawings or add colour to a monochrome picture.

Wash drawings   For scenarios, action pictures with human figures, or just as an alternative treatment to add interest in a brochure, the wash drawing is often used. In certain cases it can be just as effective as the airbrush drawing while not as expensive to produce, or in turn it can be used to freely express the subject without too much detail. Some examples are shown in Figures 4.22 and 4.23.

Pencil drawing   Form and tonal effects can be added to line drawings by pencil shading (*see* Figure 4.24). Pencil or charcoal drawings have to be treated as half-tones for reproduction.

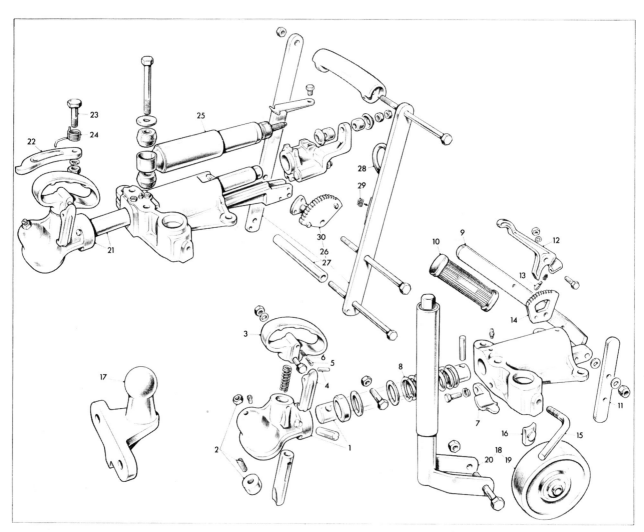

Fig. 4.24   Line drawing with pencil shading.

Planning a Series   At the planning stage of a technical manual the feasibility of producing a series of illustrations developed from one basic perspective illustration of the equipment should be studied. A considerable amount of equipment is suitable for this approach, even though this may not be immediately obvious.

Perspective pencil sketches should first be made to see if there is a common viewpoint suitable to cover all the illustrations that are likely to be required, such as operational, descriptive and servicing. Time taken initially will be well spent as the returns in economy and efficiency can be high.

Once a suitable angle has been chosen a basic outline drawing should be prepared from which every other drawing can be constructed. This drawing could be enlarged or reduced to any size; also a transparency could be made for the drawing office staff, who probably will not realize the value of such a drawing until they get it.

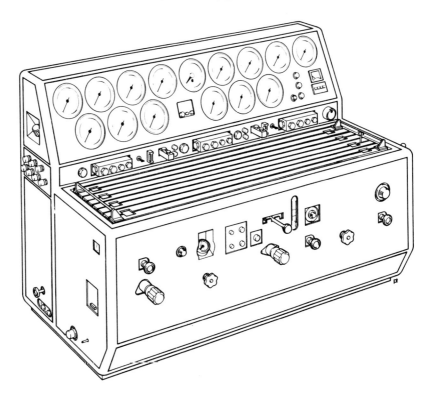

Fig. 4.25   Test bench external view.

In the example shown, an external view of a hydraulic test bench was drawn from the basic outline drawing (*see* Figure 4.25). This illustration, suitably annotated, was used to support descriptive, operational and maintenance material. In Figure 4.26 internal details have been added to locate the main components, and this illustration was also used in several places in the manual. Figure 4.27 shows the basic outline drawing to which has been added the electrical system, to show wiring layout. Here it was necessary to include an inset detail from another view. A version of this drawing with numbers was also used in the spares list section of the manual. Figure 4.28 shows the seals in the hydraulic system, and the same drawing was renumbered for pipe couplings and again for hoses and sight-glass assembly.

The flexibility of application once the base drawing has been determined is considerable. It can be used in part to show a detail as in Figure

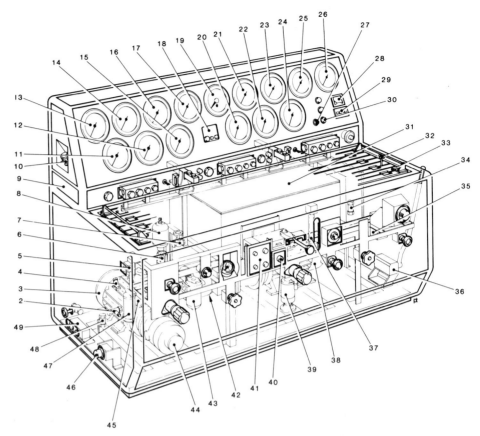

Fig. 4.26   Test bench internal details.

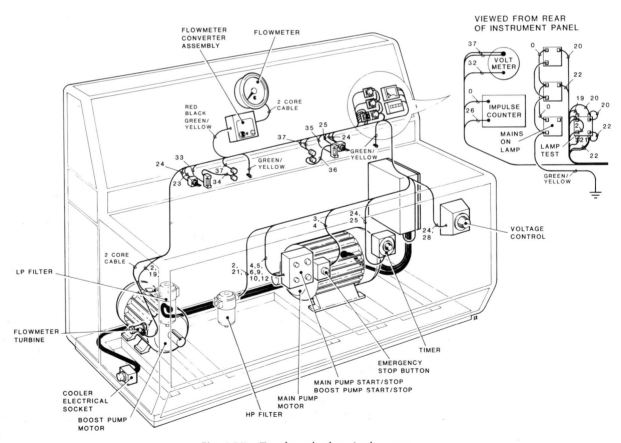

Fig. 4.27   Test bench electrical system.

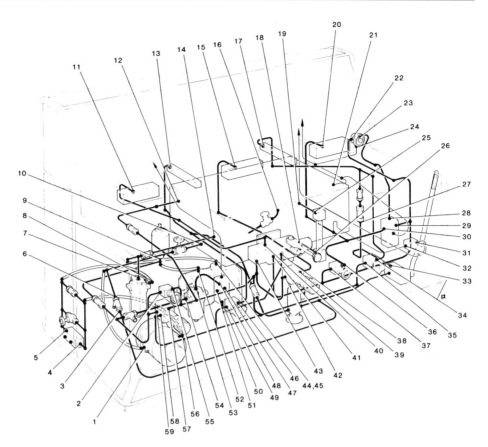

Fig. 4.28   Test bench hydraulic seals.

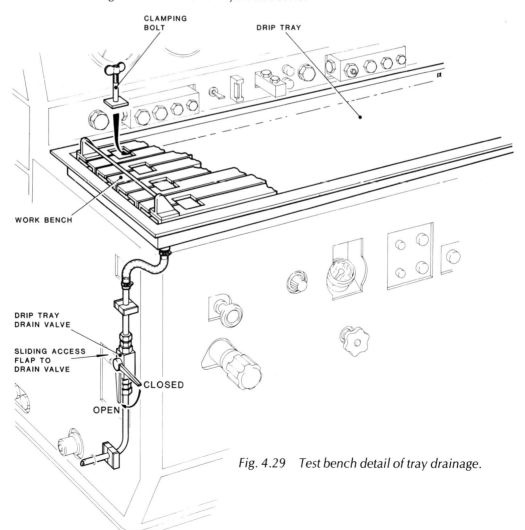

Fig. 4.29   Test bench detail of tray drainage.

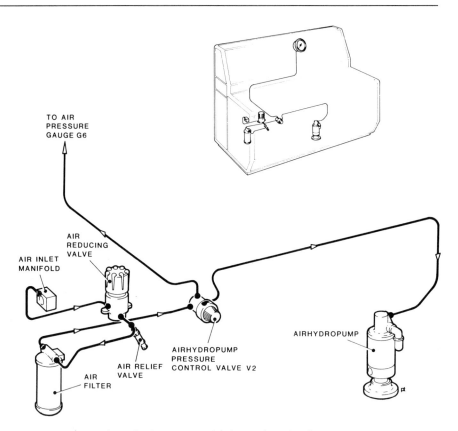

Fig. 4.30   Test bench air system with inset showing location.

4.29 or a system can be isolated as in Figure 4.30 with the addition of a locational view if required. Here again both these illustrations were used with numbers for the parts list.

The addition of details or modification to the equipment is greatly simplified by this method. The starting point of every illustration is known, and therefore modifications do not have to be done by the original illustrator, and can be carried out by a whole team if necessary.

In this particular example 21 illustrations were used throughout the manual, all based on the one master drawing. In addition, other versions were made into wall charts, production drawings, packing details, training slides, etc. The cost of illustrating the manual was reduced in two ways, firstly by greater efficiency, and secondly because it was shared by other departments by the savings they had made. Also the status of the publications department was enhanced by the realization of their value to the company.

TECHNIQUES AND EQUIPMENT

The purpose of this section is to help trainee or newly trained illustrators apply their skills in a commercial environment, and to make the uninitiated aware of just what is involved in the preparation of illustrations for publication.

A study should be made of Chapters 2 and 3, and the author and illustrator should work in close liaison when interpreting the brief, gathering facts and presenting them efficiently within the specification required.

Where to Start? Whatever the equipment to be illustrated, it must have been manufactured by someone, and this is the starting point for gathering information. Seek out all information available such as drawings, parts lists, photographs and ask questions of anyone who has first-hand knowledge of the equipment.

At the earliest possible stage get to see the equipment, sketch details and take photographs.

Use of Camera The illustrator does not have to be an expert photographer, but the camera is an excellent fast recorder of information and can be an invaluable aid. Whenever there is an opportunity to record a stage in the build of the equipment, especially if changes or variations are possible, it is useful to take photographs. Such an opportunity may never occur again.

A photograph can also be used as a basis for an illustration, and even if the quality is not good, an enlarged print can be traced. This is particularly helpful when manufacturer's drawings are not available and so cannot be used to construct a drawing.

Drawing System Get to know the manufacturer's drawing system so that you know just where to find the information you require. Be sure that all modifications are made available as soon as possible so that you know just what is going on. Make a careful study of all the drawings so as to absorb as much information as possible, and seek clarification on anything you do not understand.

How does it Work? Remember that a technical illustration usually has to show how something works or is constructed; it is essential, therefore, that the illustrator should know this too. Of course, he cannot be expected to be a technological expert on every subject, but sometimes the solution is as simple as having a unit dismantled to clarify its function.

Starting the Illustration When all the preliminary investigations have been made and the brief is clear, the illustration can be started. Remember, however, that time spent planning an illustration, before actually starting, can avoid getting so far and then having to start again because it does not seem to be working out.

Perspective The transferring of lines on paper from a two dimensional aspect into three dimensions is both fascinating and time consuming. It can be done by pure geometry or be subject to a certain amount of imaginative guesswork, and sometimes it is impossible to tell the difference.

Whatever method is used, commercial pressure demands that the final result is arrived at as quickly as possible, and so every illustrator looks for short cuts. Another restriction, as well as time, is the amount of space required to construct a perspective drawing. A drawing that would comfortably fit within an A3 area, depending on the angles chosen, would need at least one vanishing point beyond the limits of an average drawing board.

Scale perspective The problems of space can sometimes be solved by the use of scale perspective. It is always advisable anyway before starting a large illustration to make several small sketches of the equipment from which the best viewpoint can be selected. When the best angle has been chosen, an accurate drawing can be made, either at the same size as the sketch, or the largest possible to allow the vanishing points to fit on the drawing board. This drawing can then be scaled up to the size required using proportional dividers, Grant projector (*see* the section 'Equipment') or photographic enlargement.

Scale grid   This is another method of scale perspective where a perspective grid is drawn to scale at the angle required to view the subject, and then enlarged to the size required to make the drawing. This method has the advantage that it is fairly quick, and the grid can be used again for a similar subject.

The first step is to draw a square or rectangle around each of the three orthographic views of the subject to be drawn. From these three views a scale perspective box can be drawn at the angle required to suit the subject, and then enlarged to fit the drawing area being used. Next, divide each face of the box into equal portions, the number depending on the amount of detail needed. You will now have a perspective grid drawn to fit each view of the subject, from which any point can be projected. This grid can be made more or less elaborate according to requirements.

The same method can be used to construct a grid for permanent use by drawing a cube to scale in three point perspective. Using the intersection of the three axes as centre, draw a circle around the cube. Using the same point as zero, mark a common scale along each axis that will diminish in one direction and increase in the opposite direction.

This can then be enlarged to any size and by any method, and then the cube divided to form a perspective grid, and the lines extended to the circumference of the circle.

By turning the circle so that each axis is vertical, it will be seen that the cube can be viewed from six different angles, three on the top and three from underneath. If it is drawn on a transparency and then reversed, the cube can be viewed in six more ways, making a total of twelve.

Perspective Drawing Board   The perspective drawing board is a method of drawing lines in three point perspective using a 'T' square.

The board is triangular with concave sides and the 'T' of the 'T' square is convexed to fit the sides. As the square moves along each side the angle changes in true perspective.

Another perspective grid is the frame type which allows for drawing straight on to line board if required. The drawing area has been removed into which space the line board, or whatever material is being used, can be placed. A perspective drawing can then be made using the grid lines framing the drawing area.

Isometric Projection   This is a method of projection used to portray three dimensions on orthographic drawings. The angle used is 30°, and as there is no perspective used, the drawing has a very poor pictorial quality. Other methods such as dimetric, oblique and trimetric are similar in that they are inferior substitutes for the real thing.

Inking   Line weight should be determined by the scale of reduction and type of illustration. Illustrators inevitably develop their own styles, but a certain uniformity within a single publication should be attempted, and some specifications give strict ruling on what can and cannot be done.

Technical illustrations are best drawn to a size larger than the size required for printing. This allows for more detail to be drawn and gives a sharper image when reduced. The size will vary according to the subject matter, but wherever possible it is good practice within a studio to establish a standard reduction size for all illustrations (this is 150% or 200% of final reduction size). In this way, line weight, annotations size, instructions to printer, etc., will be standard for all drawings.

Care should always be taken on illustrations for reduction to see that there are no lines that may close up due to being too close, or break up if too fine; also check for areas that may lose clarity because of too much solid black.

Orthographic Drawings   Because it is drawn in two dimensions, the definition of areas on an orthographic drawing by line weight has to be considered. If the profile of the subject is the main feature required, such as on drawings showing overall dimensions, or installation drawings (*see* Figure 4.9), the details can be kept to a minimum with a fairly fine weight of line. The profile can then be outlined with a strong line (attenuated background) giving a clear indication of the area of space that the object fills.

Shadow Line Technique   Where details need to be shown on an orthographic drawing, the shadow line can be applied; and for some authorities this is specified (*see* Chapter 10). In this technique a heavier line is used on all the bottom and right-hand edges of the object and has the effect of giving the object form and depth by indicating the third dimension. It is also possible to 'read' an illustration prepared in this way and determine the form of the object, although only seeing it in two dimensions. For example, Figure 4.31(*a*) shows a block with a projecting shaft. Figure 4.31(*b*) shows the same block with a hole instead of a shaft. View A on both figures would be the same, but by using the shadow line it is possible to determine which is the block with the shaft and which one has the hole, Figure 4.31(*c*). Figures 4.10 and 4.11 show orthographic drawings using the shadow line technique.

On sectional views, the edges of material that have been cut should be indicated by stippling to represent the texture of the material (*see* the section 'Stippling').

Shading   The technique of shading on a line drawing is as old as the craft of making woodcuts from which it developed, and the expertly shaded illustration can be very pleasing. In general, however, it is best kept to a minimum, and the treatment reserved for times when it is necessary to accentuate certain features or clarify areas.

Mechanical Tints   Mechanical tints are pre-printed self-adhesive sheets of tonal patterns that can be applied to line drawings or artwork. There is a wide range to choose from for all kinds of applications.

The finer grades of dot patterns can be used instead of hand shading to show form or texture, but over use should be avoided and one pattern should never be laid on another.

Areas on artwork where tints are to be laid down should be free from

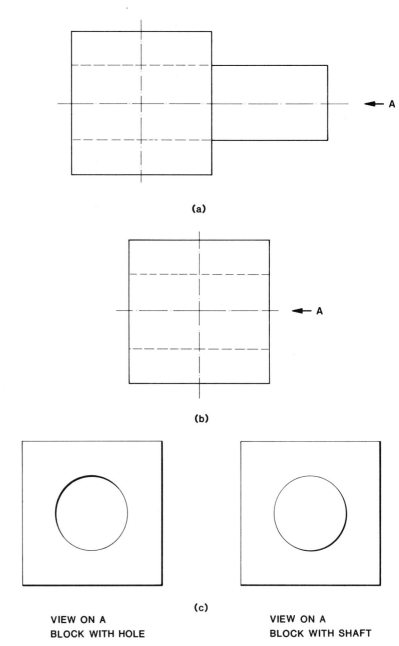

VIEW ON A
BLOCK WITH HOLE

VIEW ON A
BLOCK WITH SHAFT

Fig. 4.31   Shadow line technique.

any marks that could be reproduced, and the tint should be well burnished without damage.

Tints can also be added to charts and diagrams, as an alternative to colour, to accentuate or differentiate between areas.

The manufacturer's guidance for suitable percentage of reduction should be carefully followed when choosing tints to give a tonal effect, so that quality is maintained when reproduced.

Stippling   The technique of hand stippling is an art in itself and many illustrators become very proficient in its use, producing whole illustrations in this form.

Its most common use on technical illustrations is to indicate on sections and cutaways the edges of material that have been cut (*see* Figures 4.10 and 4.11). Some authorities specify this instead of the cross hatching used on production drawings, and it is certainly less confusing, being in direct contrast to the lines on the drawing. It should, however, be clearly defined for each part of the section it is indicating so that it is possible to differentiate between one area and another.

Stippling can also be used to indicate rubber or foam textures as it can be graded very effectively from dark to light.

Photo-retouching and Airbrushing   The use of the airbrush for photo-retouching, airbrush drawing and general airbrush artwork is a specialized technique that should only be carried out by the fully trained or trainees under supervision, and the advice given here is considered useful for general guidance under these conditions.

Airbrush   The airbrush is a precision instrument and should be handled as such. Each part is very costly to renew and should be treated with care to prolong its life.

The part most subject to damage is the needle, which is sharpened to a fine point and therefore very delicate. Whenever it is removed it should be carefully examined and, if damaged, renewed. A hooked needle can in turn damage the floating nozzle which is even more expensive to renew, and vital to the efficient operation of the airbrush. The floating nozzle is part of a matched set and cannot be renewed without the outer nozzle in which it seats.

Air supply   It is essential to have a supply of compressed air to operate the airbrush and there are small compressors made for this purpose. It may be possible in some technical publications departments to connect up to a main air supply, in which case a reducing valve should be fitted to control the pressure at around 35 lbf/in^2 (2.46 kgf/cm^2), which is the normal operating pressure of the airbrush. It is also desirable to have a water separator to remove moisture from the air supply in the circuit.

There are other sources of supply that can be used on a less permanent basis such as:

A large compressed air bottle or container – this would also need a reducing valve.
Aerosol can – made specially for the airbrush and ideal for portable use.

But in both these cases they would be uneconomical to use continuously.

Photo-retouching   Only the minimum of retouching necessary should be used on any photograph. Do not get carried away.

Screen and process to be used   Before retouching or preparing artwork with the airbrush, the artist should know the method of printing, screen size and reproduction size to be used.

The process of screening continuous tone originals is dealt with in Chapter 7.

The screen used in the process camera to make the dot pattern for the tonal effect will vary according to whatever the printing process and paper is to be. Screens are classified by the line rulings which make the dot patterns, and these vary between 55 to 175 lines to the inch.

Most technical publications that include half-tones are printed by photolitho on a coated paper and the most commonly used screen for this type of work is 133 lines per inch.

Photographs for retouching are best if they are unglazed glossy prints, a little larger than reproduction size (the retoucher should be provided with two prints so that one can be used for reference). If a large reduction is required, or if artwork is likely to be used many times at varying reductions, it is better to keep the tones at the lighter end of the tonal range.

Ink and paints   Only water colour paints and inks recommended for the airbrush should be used. Inks and paints with coarse pigments and impurities will cause excessive wear and can damage the nozzle.

Masking   Low tack masking paper that is specially prepared for retouching should be used. Never use any other type of adhesive paper or tape which may damage the surface of the photograph or artwork, or sometimes leaves traces of adhesive behind. Masking paper can be bought in sheets and wide rolls, and it is usually more economical and time-saving to completely cover a piece of artwork or photograph with masking paper and then remove the areas that need to be sprayed. Always be careful, however, not to damage the surface – use a sharp scalpel with a light pressure and carefully remove the mask when finished.

Preparing Artwork   *Illustrations*   Traditionally line drawings have always been prepared on line board, which has a smooth white surface ideal for taking a clean black ink line applied by drawing pen, ruling pen or brush. Line board is very hardwearing and can withstand erasing and even scraping with a razor blade.

The method is to make a pencil drawing on tracing or drawing paper and then rub the back with graphite, jeweller's rouge or a substance that will transfer a mark onto the board when the pencil drawing is traced or 'pushed-through'.

Alternatively a sheet of 'pushing-through' paper could be made-up and used several times over so that the back of the drawing is left clear. The important thing is to ensure that the substance used to make the copy is not greasy or too messy, which would interfere with inking in and could not be cleaned-up afterwards.

The drawback of this method is that in effect, the illustration is drawn three times – once on the tracing paper, then to push it through on to the line board and finally when inked in. Also it is not so easy to make a copy of the original for checking, reference, etc.

The most popular method today is to use a translucent draughting film laid over the pencil drawing which is then inked straight on to the film. This produces an original which can be dyeline copied for checking, etc., before being reproduced for printing.

It is advisable to use drawing ink made specially for this film and identified with the letters 'TT', which is quick drying, adheres to the film, but allows for erasions to be made by the light application of a scalpel blade or special ink rubbers.

Camera-ready artwork   With photosetting and litho printing becoming the most widely used form of reproduction today, most artwork is now prepared ready for the process camera and platemaking. Each page of the book is prepared as a piece of artwork exactly as it will be printed. It can also be grouped with other pages as one large piece of artwork that will be printed on one sheet of paper and then cut or folded in whatever way the book is to be made-up and bound. This, however, should be by arrangement with the printer, because it may be more suitable for him to do this at the platemaking stage.

Whichever way it is to be done, everything to appear on each page of the book must be pasted-up in its exact position. This is best done on card or board, using rubber solution which allows for repositioning and the easy removal of any surplus adhesive.

The mounting card or board should be larger than page size, so that the corner marks of each page can be drawn on as trim guides; any instructions, fold lines, registration marks, etc., should be in the outside margin.

The paste-up must be clean and free of any marks other than those that are to appear on the finished page. The text to be pasted-up should be trimmed using a sharp scalpel and steel straight edge and care taken to avoid making too many small cuts that may be picked up by the camera.

Good quality photo prints must be made of all the illustrations at reproduction size. If any are to be inserted into the text they should be stripped into their appropriate pages so that each page will look exactly as it will appear in the publication. Full page illustrations are pasted onto a page along with the figure number and title and anything else that is to appear on that page.

Half-tones   Where there are to be half-tone inserts, the area that is to be half-toned should be outlined with a fine line (keyline). If the half-tone is squared-up, this keyline will appear as either a square or rectangle to the exact dimensions of the half-tone. If the half-tone is a cut-out then the keyline will follow the exact shape of the cut-out half-tone. Instructions to the printer should be written within the keyline area to 'insert half-tone A' or whatever mark is used to identify the picture. This same mark, of course, will appear on the photograph or artwork, clear of the illustration area, that is to be half-toned so that it is clear to the printer exactly where it is to go.

Dot for dot   The process described in the previous paragraph is the most desirable, as it allows the printer to strip the half-tone negative into the negative of the whole page, which is then made into the printing plate. It is possible, however, to have a positive made from the half-tone negative, which is then pasted-up in the same way as a line illustration. This is called dot for dot. In the same way, if the original photograph or artwork is not available it is possible to copy a half-tone print providing it is good quality. This method does not guarantee good quality reproduction and should only be used if there is no other way.

Colour separation   If a photograph or illustration in full colour is to be used in a publication, the separation of each colour for printing is done by a process camera using special filters (*see* Chapter 7). The procedure for preparing the artwork will be the same as for half-tones and the printer must be supplied with a good colour print or transparency of the photograph or, in the case of an illustration, the original.

When a page is to be printed in just one or two additional colours, the artwork for that page should give instructions to the printer as to exactly what is wanted. Registration marks (usually crosses) should be made outside the illustration area and a transparent overlay (tracing paper or something similar) for each colour laid over the artwork. Indicate on each overlay what colour it represents and then outline everything on the artwork that is to be printed in that colour. In addition to the overlays the printer should be supplied with a colour guide for the whole page showing him what colours are to be printed.

On some illustrations, such as system diagrams, where certain details are to be printed in colour, it may be better for the illustrator to prepare the separation. For this purpose the overlay should be made on draughting film, and the area to be coloured and the page registration marks inked in with black ink exactly to fit the illustration. If there is to be any text or wording in the same colour it should be pasted on the overlay in the correct position. In this case all the printer will need is the colour guide.

Reversing-out   When a solid area of black or colour is wanted, it is only necessary to outline the area on the artwork with a black line. The printer will then reverse this when he makes his plate so that it will be a black area with a white outline. The same applies to lettering that needs to appear on a solid background.

An example of this and other preparations discussed can be seen in Figures 4.32, 4.33 and 4.34.

Reduction marking   When artwork has been prepared for the printer, the reproduction size must be indicated. Most camera-ready artwork will be actual size (100%), but on artwork that is larger than reproduction size, the reduction must be marked in some way. If the artwork is twice actual size it can be indicated as a 2:1 reduction, or a measurement can be taken between two extreme points on the artwork, divided by two and this dimension marked as the reduction between these two points. Printers usually work in percentages expressed either by the amount of reduction or to what percentage reduced. For example a 2:1 reduction is 50% and in this case the percentage is the same either way. In the following examples it will be seen that the percentage 'reduced by' added to the percentage 'reduced to' must be 100% every time.

Ratio of artwork size to reduced size	Reduced by	Reduced to
4:1	75%	25%
2:1	50%	50%
1½:1	33⅓%	66⅔%

Whatever percentage is used it must be made clear to the printer.

Aids   The skill of the technical illustrator is his most valuable asset and it used to be considered that any illustrator who needed anything other than the few basic tools of his craft was somehow lessening that skill.

Today there are many aids the illustrator can use to make his job quicker and more efficient, and it would be foolish not to take advantage of them. However, aids must be used *with* skill, not *instead* of – the craft must not be allowed to be forgotten.

Pencils   There are many excellent makes of clutch pencils on the market today with varying thicknesses of lead. These are particularly useful for their constant line thickness and of course they do not need sharpening.

Pens The drawing pen with tubular nib and ink reservoir is now widely used in place of the old flexible nib pen which had to be dipped into the ink. There are many makes and sizes which give constant line thickness for many applications. Manufacturer's guidance should be followed for cleaning and type of ink so that they are always working at maximum efficiency.

Ellipse guides The use of ellipse guides or templates has increased as more have become available. Only the precision makes with true ellipses and smoothly finished edges should be used. They are usually the most expensive, but with careful handling will last indefinitely.

Grant projector The Grant projector accurately enlarges or reduces an image which can then either be traced or copied on to light-sensitive paper. It consists of a moving platform, which takes the image to be copied, and an adjustable lens; both platform and lens are controlled by handwheels on the front of the projector. The enlarged or reduced image is projected on to a glass viewing panel on which tracing paper can be laid for copying. A canopy over the viewing panel keeps out surrounding light so that only the projected image, which is lit from inside the projector, can be seen on the panel. Additional lights can be added so that a photocopy can be made by placing light-sensitive paper over the viewing panel, which has a light-proof cover. This does, of course, require additional developing equipment.

Transparencies for Overhead Projectors

Good quality overhead projector transparencies can be produced on most makes of thermal and xerographic copiers by the use of special transparency film, as recommended by the manufacturer of the particular machine. The film replaces the normal paper in the paper tray and the machine is operated in the normal way. This method of making transparencies is most suitable for high quality artwork with clear black lines on a white background. Any defects will be magnified during projection. Although the quality of the transparency produced in this way is not quite as good as a transparency produced by photography, it is much cheaper and quicker when a suitable copier is available in the department.

The transparencies produced can be mounted or not, as desired, and coloured in using water-soluble or permanent ink pens. If water-soluble inks are used, the coloured portions can be removed and filled in during lectures if desired, as the black printed image is not water-soluble. A spirit-based cleaning fluid, as used for removing permanent ink from the transparency, will tend to smudge or remove completely the printed image from the transparency.

Progressive Stages from Design to Final Artwork

Some of the techniques and preparations discussed in this chapter are shown in Figures 4.32, 4.33 and 4.34. Figure 4.32 shows a simple design rough, often called a visual, for the cover of a brochure on steel silos and containers. The purpose of the visual is to provide everyone concerned with a fair representation of the final job. From the basic design visual it can be decided what artwork must be prepared, and the visual can also be used as a printer's guide at the printing stage. The area shown black on the design was in fact printed blue on the original but the artwork is the same whatever the colour, except that the instruction to the printer would say

Fig. 4.32   Design visual for brochure cover.

blue or whatever colour instead of black, and of course the design visual would show the colour as well.

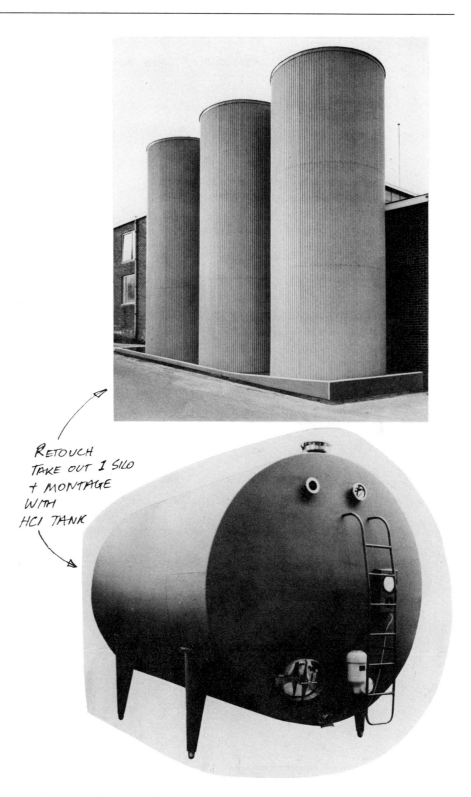

Fig. 4.33   Photographs for cover montage.

Figure 4.33 shows the photographs used in the preparation of the montage and Figure 4.34 shows the final artwork with all the instructions to the printer.

Fig. 4.34   Final artwork for brochure cover.

READING ORTHOGRAPHIC DRAWINGS

Although manufacturers today find it necessary to economize on the number of production drawings they produce – particularly general arrangements – the orthographic, or blue print as it used to be called, is still the major source of information for the technical publications department. (An orthographic drawing is a drawing having the point of sight at infinity.)

Many illustrators either started work, or have spent some time of their working life, in a drawing office. Some may have acquired a working knowledge of the orthographic drawing by workshop or technical college training. Other technical publications personnel, even without this background, seem to find no difficulty in understanding production drawings. There are, however, those to whom the orthographic drawing, particularly the geometry of projection, seems shrouded in mystery. Hopefully, this section will help explain what, to the initiated, may seem elementary.

Angles of Projection

The main area of confusion in understanding an orthographic drawing seems to be the angle of projection. Space can be divided by two planes, the vertical, such as a wall or a fence, and the horizontal, such as a floor or a ceiling. The crossing of these two planes would form four right angles (*see* Figure 4.35). If an object is placed in the first angle and viewed from the right or the top, the views projected on to the vertical and horizontal planes will be in first-angle projection. If the same object is placed in the third angle and again viewed from the right or the top, but this time assuming the two planes to be transparent, the views seen on the two planes are in third-angle projection (*see* Figure 4.36).

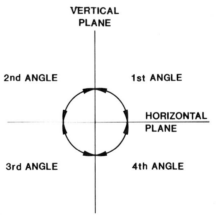

Fig. 4.35   Angles of projection.

In both cases the direction of view is the same, but in the first-angle projection the object is between the viewer and the plane, whereas in the third-angle projection, the plane is between the viewer and the object. Figure 4.37 shows three views drawn in first-angle projection, and Figure 4.38 shows three views drawn in third-angle projection. From these two examples, it can be seen that in first-angle projection the plan or top view is under or at the bottom of the front elevation and the right-hand end elevation is on the left-hand of the front elevation. In the third-angle projection these positions are reversed.

A simple rule is that in first-angle projection views are always drawn on

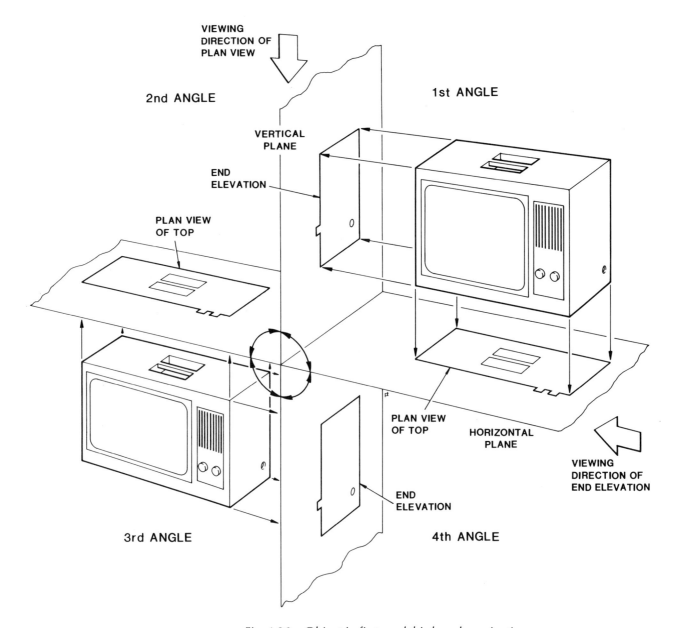

Fig. 4.36   Object in first- and third-angle projections.

the side of the object furthest from the direction of view, and in third-angle projection views are drawn on the side of the object adjacent to the side being viewed.

The advantage of third-angle projection is particularly noticeable on a very large or long object as the view drawn is adjacent to the end being viewed.

This can of course be achieved in first-angle projection, but a note must be added to indicate this departure from the projection being used.

Sectional Views   To show the internal construction of an object a sectional view is taken. This view shows what would be seen if an object is sliced at a particular point. For example, if a slice of bread is cut from a loaf and the loaf viewed with the slice removed, this is a true section of the loaf at that point. In the same way, a sliced loaf represents a series of sections taken along the length of the loaf.

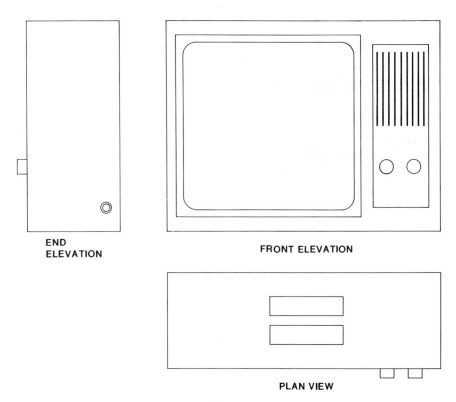

Fig. 4.37 *Three views in first-angle projection.*

A section can be taken in any direction and through any plane, but it must be clearly indicated on the drawing.

The areas of the object that have been cut must be indicated in some way. Metal and solid material is usually shown cross-hatched; stone or concrete is usually represented as in fact it would look.

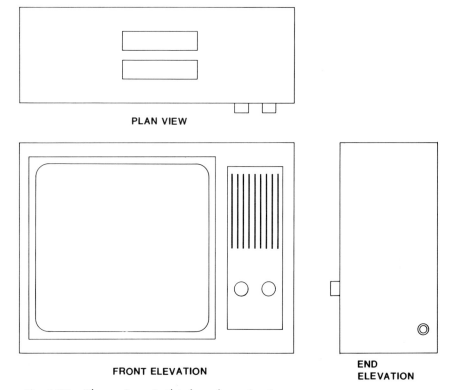

Fig. 4.38 *Three views in third-angle projection.*

If the cut only goes to the centre, it is called a half-section, and this should be noted on the view and only half the view cross-hatched.

Lines   The shape of the object on an orthographic drawing is shown in a continuous line of medium weight. Hidden shapes, such as thickness of material, holes, etc., are shown with a broken line. Cross-hatching, dimension arrows and leader lines should be fine continuous lines, and centrelines, projection lines and reference lines are fine chain-dotted lines.

When an orthographic drawing is used for an illustration it should be presented as described in the section Techniques and Equipment (*see* page 78).

LAYOUT AND DESIGN

Design is the blending of two main ingredients – the functional and the aesthetic. Good design is when these two ingredients are used in just the right proportions to suit the purpose of the subject.

The functional aspect is more easy to define; tests can be made to see how well something works. The aesthetic relates to how something affects the senses, such as sight and touch, and is therefore more dependent on the individual tastes of the viewer or user.

Printed matter, such as a technical or scientific publication, is, by definition, mainly functional, and this should be reflected in the design. The message being conveyed should be without distraction.

The layout and design of printed matter is the work of the graphic designer, whose job is to bring together the written word, known as text or copy, with the pictures or illustrations, and present them in whatever form is most suitable for the subject matter.

The designer produces a rough or visual which is a sample of how the finished product will look when printed, and should indicate the type-faces, colour, when used, and layout of a sample page.

Whether or not a graphic designer is used depends largely on the project itself, but in any case everyone involved in a publication, and particularly the illustrator, should have a feeling for design.

Layout   The basic layout of a page will of course depend on the specification being followed throughout the book (*see* Chapters 10 and 3), and where the same page layout is to be used many times, as in a large publication or series of publications, it is advisable to have a quantity of blank pages pre-printed with the layout in a light blue ink that will not photograph. This is particularly useful when camera-ready artwork is to be prepared, and apart from a considerable saving of time in not having to mark up each page, it ensures that the format is accurately followed for both text and illustrations.

As far as the text is concerned, once the pattern of a page is established, it can be strictly followed without the possibility of too much individual variance. What goes on within the specified area of an illustration is, however, often subject to abuse and lack of thought.

Again the basic question should be asked: *What is the purpose of the illustration?* If it is purely functional, such as a servicing manual illustration, then this should be the strongest influence in the layout and design of the illustration and annotations. If it is promotional material such as a sales leaflet or exhibition illustration, then the eye-catching quality needs to be given more prominence.

For example, on a parts list illustration every item listed has to be clearly identified and numbered so that the list and illustration can be easily cross-referenced (*see* Figure 4.28). There has to be organization in the layout to avoid confusion. Wherever possible, the numbers should be in consecutive order, starting on the left of the picture at about the seven o'clock position and continuing around in a clockwise direction. The leader lines should be as short as possible to allow the numbers to be clear of the illustration, go direct to the item indicated and avoid crossing too many other items. This is an example of good design. On the other hand, for a promotional illustration for a brochure or leaflet, it may be necessary to highlight certain selling features of the equipment to make them stand out from the rest to attract the viewer.

Annotations The method of annotating illustrations will vary according to general practice and application. Some specifications have fairly loose guidelines where annotations are concerned.

It has always been the convention that capital letters are used for notices, filling forms, instructions and annotations on drawings, etc., possibly because all these tasks were originally done by hand and the capital letter suffers less from distortion than the lower case. Also, with the size of type usually used for annotations, it is easier to line up capitals than lower case, even with more sophisticated techniques like transfer lettering. The convention has carried on into this age of instant lettering, although research has shown that a word in all capitals is less legible. This certainly is the case with large areas of type because the reader recognizes words and phrases by their shape and texture, and this is less possible with words in all capitals (imagine reading this page of text if it were set in all capital letters).

Now that it is becoming common practice to set annotations either by composer or some form of transfer machine, perhaps it is time to rethink the subject and try to establish a standard throughout industry.

Most of the figures used in this book, and in particular this chapter, have been taken as working samples of illustrating technique from different sources. So that comparisons can be made no attempt has been made to make them uniform. Perhaps there is a case to be made for the all-capital annotations – at least it is a simple standard to follow.

Typography With the advent of word processors and photo typesetters, typographic layout has become more sophisticated, and yet more easily available to the uninitiated.

Typographic design is a science in itself, and cannot be taught in a few paragraphs of a book like this (*see also* Chapter 7). However, it is possible to follow the main principles of good typographic design without making an extensive study of the subject. Basically, typography is the choice and arrangement of typefaces on a page to suit the purpose required. Here again the functional approach is desirable, particularly with scientific and technical material.

Consider the design of letterheads, compliment slips, invoices, etc. They all bear the company's name, address, what it does and other information about the company. They are all sent through the post, copied and filed. Already a functional pattern starts to emerge. In the case of letterheaded notepaper, it usually has to be folded to suit the size of an envelope and the area for typing the letter allowed for.

Many companies have a symbol or logo which immediately identifies the company, and this too must be taken into account by the graphic designer. But the final design can have many applications, and is thus subject to much discussion and possible disagreement.

Whatever the symbol used, it should be recognizable, and instantly identify the company it represents. It may have to be blown up to be displayed over an exhibition stand, or reduced to fit a visiting card, but in either case the initial impact should be the same. For example, Figure 4.39 shows the symbol of the Institute of Scientific and Technical Communicators, which is based on the initial letters and therefore should be legible at whatever size it is reproduced. Symmetry in a logo greatly facilitates its use in a wide variety of applications.

Fig. 4.39   Logo.

Beware of changing fashion   There are two distinct areas of fashion in typographical design. One is changing almost daily, so that it is possible to tell within a week or two when something was designed. The other is the truer reflection of the steady change in the pattern of life itself. If the material lends itself to the former – then use it by all means, but regard it as instantly disposable and do not expect it to last. The latter is more suitable for material that needs to be kept a long while without dating.

Choice of type   In many cases this will be determined by the specification (*see* Chapter 10), or perhaps by an already established house style. If not, the starting point is to decide what job it has to do.

In a publication such as a novel that contains many pages of uninterrupted reading matter, the only breaks in the text are likely to be chapters and paragraphs. The whole texture of the page and the ease with which it is read depends on the shape and spacing of each word and the spaces between the words and the lines. In such cases the serif face is the most commonly used, because the texture is easier on the eye and the formation of each word more easily absorbed by the reader. In technical publications, however, there is usually a more tabulated structure to the page because it contains a number of facts, short statements and headings, etc. For this sort of work the sans serif typeface is very often more suitable as there is usually a wider range in one face or family of type. This allows for more variation when making distinctions between sections, headings, procedures, warnings, etc., and the many other divisions of text required in technical manuals.

Whatever the choice of typeface the important factor is whether the reader can take in, without distraction, what is being conveyed to him.

Grid The appearance of a complete page depends as much on the amount and balance of the surrounding space as it does on the quality and relationship of the print and pictures.

A good practice to assist the arrangement is to draw a grid the same size as the page area with the width and the length divided into equal parts. The divisions can be made more or less as required, but each cell of the grid will be in proportion to the whole page. The matter to be laid out can then be moved around on the grid while areas of space such as margins are considered.

Marking-up Whatever the method of printing to be used in a publication, and whoever has been responsible for typography and layout, the printer or typesetter must be clearly briefed (*see* Chapter 8).

Copy for typesetting should be typed as near to the finished style as possible within the limits of the typewriter, and anything that could mislead the typesetter should be avoided, e.g. breaking a word at the end of a line, underlining headings unless required, or using capitals unless required.

The copy can then be marked-up with instructions to the printer or typesetter accordingly. For this purpose a coloured marker should be used so that it is clear what are instructions and what is copy to be typeset. Different colours can be used to indicate different instructions, such as type of headings, change in weight of type, italics, etc.

The extent of detail of the mark-up will depend on what the printer or typesetter requires, but all concerned must be clear, before typesetting starts, exactly what typeface and point size is being used; the 'leading'* – or distance between the lines; the column widths; and whether the columns are to be justified or not. Remember, it is a lot more economical to have a sample or dummy page made up in the typeface and layout you require, than it is to reject copy once it has been typeset.

TRAINING

Technical illustrating in whatever field it is practised requires two essentials. One is the ability to draw an image and prepare it for reproduction, the other is to have a good technical knowledge of the subjects you are likely to illustrate.

If one has the ability to draw, the craft of technical illustrating can be taught, and the courses advised on page 203 should be taken.

Knowledge of the subject matter is gained by study and experience, and students should endeavour to continually increase their knowledge by both these methods.

*Leading or leading-out. The process of inserting leads between lines of type matter in order to open them out, thus presenting more white space between the printed lines (*Chambers Dictionary of Science and Technology*).

GLOSSARY OF TERMS

Annotation

Direct: The name or description of an item or an illustration, with a line (leader line) pointing directly to the item.

Indirect: A number pointing to each item on an illustration which is accompanied by a key identifying the items.

Artwork
Originally this term referred to any hand lettering or illustration that had to be copied by the process camera for blockmaking, as opposed to the type characters which were taken from the printer's case. With litho printing it refers to all material that has to be camera copied for plate-making.

Bleed
When a block or border of colour has to be printed right up to the edge of the paper, the image is produced so that it slightly overlaps the size of the final printed page. It is then printed on oversize paper and trimmed down to the final size required. The amount it is printed oversize is called the bleed.

Camera-ready
Text and illustrations prepared for the process camera, exactly as they will be reproduced when printed.

Continuous tone
The tonal range from light to dark or white to black of a photograph or illustration such as a pencil drawing, an airbrush drawing or a wash drawing.

Cut-out half-tone
A half-tone photograph or illustration with the background removed.

Duo-tone
A method of double screening a monochrome picture so that it can be printed in either two colours or two tones of the same colours.

Half-tone
A print of a continuous tone photograph or illustration reproduced as a series of dots varying in intensity to match the tonal range of the original.

Inset illustration
An illustration set in a page of text.

Landscape
An illustration or book, designed to be viewed with the longer side horizontal.

Line drawing
An illustration that consists of only black lines or mechanical tints on a white background, or the reverse, and therefore does not need screening. If required it can be printed in contrasting colours.

Lower case
The small letters such as a, b, c, etc., so-called because they were always kept in the lower box, or case of a typeface.

Upper case
Capital letters of a typeface such as A, B, C, etc., kept in upper box or case of a typeface.

Mark-up
The preparation of a page of text indicating to the printer the size of type, spacing, margins, etc., required.

Master
Original artwork from which copies can be made.

Micro-copying
Photographic reduction of documents to tiny dots, so that a large amount of material can be stored in a small space.

Microfiche
A small piece of film, usually 105 mm × 148 mm, containing multiple micro-images in a grid pattern of rows and columns. It is normally headed by titling which can be read without magnification.

Overlay
Part of an illustration drawn on transparent material, so that it can be treated separately from the rest of the illustration. The material used should be stable (not affected by atmospheric conditions) and keyed to the illustration by registration marks. For example, an unannotated illustration could have several overlays for the annotations, each in a different language.

Portrait
An illustration or book, designed to be viewed with the longer side vertical.

Process
The term used for the preparation by the camera of material for printing.

Registration marks
Marks, usually crosses, used on separate pieces of artwork that have to be keyed together to make one illustration when printed.

Squared-up half-tone
A half-tone photograph or illustration with the background made square or rectangular to whatever size required.

Acknowledgements for illustrations in Chapter 4

APV International Ltd: Figures 9, 13–15, 18–21
R. W. H. Wood, MISTC and the Barking College of Technology: Figures 1, 12, 22 and 24
Philip Thompson, AMISTC: Figures 7 and 8
HML (Engineering) Ltd, Chief Illustrator Philip Thompson: Figures 2–6, 10, 11, 16, 17, 25–30
Industrial Artists Ltd: Figure 39
Portsmouth College of Art and Design: Figure 23

CHAPTER 5

Editing

by

E. J. MARDEN

In all probability a dentist enjoys a better relationship with his patients than most editors do with their authors. The act of writing demands a considerable expenditure of nervous energy, which often generates a fierce possessiveness in the writer; so an author can be very sensitive to criticism, especially if such criticism appears to him to be arbitrary.

Persons inexperienced in editing have a tendency to introduce changes for no apparent reason, and often, in so doing, to alter meanings or introduce grammatical errors and technical inaccuracies. Any proposed alteration must be obviously essential for accuracy or highly desirable for style or clarity if it is to stand any chance of rational consideration.

However, if editing is regarded as a means of enhancing the value of the work, and hence the author's reputation, the amount of bad feeling so often generated by the editing process would appear to be somewhat paradoxical.

Before accepting an editorial task, the proposed editor should make an objective assessment of his own abilities, not only in respect of grammar, syntax and spelling, but also of his own stock of common sense, and his ability to identify a philosophy from a text and to recognize the logical development of that philosophy. The editor must have a sound confidence in his own ability to enable him to speak with conviction and authority to the author.

As the range of activities and the status and authority of 'editors' vary from firm to firm, and often from job to job, it is not possible to cover every variation in detail. This chapter has, therefore, been written with the following principally in mind:

- A person who is required to co-ordinate all publications each with the other.
- A person who is not required, or has no reason, to co-ordinate all publications each with the other.

It is hoped that this presentation will enable most editorial personnel to benefit from the text.

EDITORIAL POWERS

Before any attempt is made to edit anything, it is essential that the editor's powers are known to all parties. In addition to being known, it is as well, especially when dealing with senior personnel, to make sure that such powers will be respected.

It is customary in most organizations for heads of departments to have terms of reference, and it will be in the best interests of management to make sure that certain matters connected with its publications are controlled and monitored by knowledgeable staff. With such an emotional and expensive subject as publications, there appears to be no good reason why the editor-in-chief (who is, normally, the senior member of the publications staff) should not be delegated responsibilities and powers by the management, and also for such delegation to be made public in a tangible form, e.g. a staff directive, so that it can be used as a working document. Matters to be considered for delegation are listed in the appendix to this chapter.

Where the editor is acting as a freelance, or does not have delegated powers, he should, unless he is absolutely sure of his ground, ensure that his labours will not be in vain by reaching an understanding, and recording it in writing, before work is commenced. Such an understanding, which could be contractual, should serve to eliminate misunderstanding or recrimination which may manifest itself late in the programme, and result in unacceptable reworking and consequential delays.

It is essential that the editor should not be overawed or intimidated by the originators of any document he is asked to edit. On occasions, a document may be produced after long and arduous negotiations, sometimes at international level, and when it is handed to the editor he may be warned not to alter it or find anything wrong with it, as 'everybody understands it' or some such platitude. With such a document there are a few extra considerations.

(a) The wording could have been arrived at without the advice of a skilled communicator.
(b) The language of the document could be foreign to some of the participants.
(c) Face could be lost, if the document were to be severely manhandled by the editor.
(d) The editor could be more unpopular than usual, simply by discharging his responsibilities.

In such cases, the editor should draw attention to his delegated responsibilities, and make it quite plain that he intends to discharge them unless instructed in writing not to do so. Where he has no such delegated responsibilities he should insist on a written definition of the scope of his activities. Professional integrity should never yield to expediency or self-interest, however tempting such courses may appear to be at the time. As usual, Shakespeare has the right words:

Who steals my purse steals trash; 'tis something, nothing;
'Twas mine, 'tis his, and has been slave to thousands;
But he that filches from me my good name
Robs me of that which not enriches him,
And makes me poor indeed.

CONSISTENCY

It is as well for the editor to establish, for each field in which he is expected to work, a list of those terms which are likely to be written out in different ways, e.g. landing gear/undercarriage; power-unit/engine; fin/vertical stabilizer; and to decide which term is to be used. Ideally, terms in the appropriate British Standard should be adopted, unless any are defined differently by the author or within the organization.

The list could also contain instructions on any other matters or terms which need to be expressed consistently, e.g. 'sea level' with or without a hyphen; the use of hyphens generally; acceptable abbreviations, for instance, lbf/in^2 and not p.s.i. or lb/sq. in; a system for marking footnotes; a system for discriminating between different lines in graphs; the use of stops in abbreviations.

The list need not necessarily be limited to technical terms, but may be extended to include the latest vogue-words and phrases, such as 'meaningful', 'escalate', 'consult with', 'on-going situation', 'engineering-wise', etc., *ad nauseam*, together with those grammatical constructions which will not be acceptable for inclusion in any document which is to be seen outside the organization, e.g. double negation, split infinitives, dangling participles, sentences ended with a preposition, personification, slang expressions, profanity.

Memorizing the list to ensure instant recall can be a gradual process, but it is a help if the editor has taken part in the decision-making, and has prepared the list himself. Fortunately, the appearance in the text of the latest vogue-words and grammatical lapses so offends the senses that they tend to give themselves up without a fight.

Where the editor is responsible for co-ordination of all the publications issued by an organization, as much of the list as is practical should be incorporated in any house rules. It is essential (especially where authors may not bother to consult the list, or may not even realize that there is a need to refer to it) to pay particular attention to consistency, otherwise the possibility of misinterpretation may be introduced (*see also* Chapter 8).

Even where co-ordination is not a requirement, the use of a consistent vocabulary is no disadvantage, as it will tend to highlight synonyms and give the editor the chance to decide whether such synonyms and any 'elegant variations' thereof, serve any useful purpose. It is best, when accepting freelance work, to agree with the customer the extent of use of standard terms.

Situations may arise in which the editor is tempted to sacrifice consistency for the sake of smoother reading. If, for instance, it has been decided that the correct term is 'the one-power-unit-inoperative Take-off Net Flight Path' it can be a temptation to lapse into 'the Flight Path' or something similar where the term appears frequently in a sentence or paragraph; in such cases it may be acceptable to qualify the term, when it first appears, with an expression on the lines of '(hereinafter referred to as "the Flight Path")'.

'Due to', which is admittedly now included in the *Concise Oxford Dictionary* as a synonym for 'as a result of' or 'resulting from', and personification ('whose wheels are square' instead of 'the wheels of which are square') are also temptations for expediency over integrity. Although some 'authorities' may sanction the use of an alternative, mostly on the grounds of expediency, it is for the editor to decide how far he is prepared to lower his own standards. However, as technical documents are not intended for light reading (although they need not lack literary merit) it is best to repeat the correct term throughout, and thus eliminate any possibility of misunderstanding. Misinterpretation by the reader of a specification or a safety requirement could have expensive and acrimonious repercussions.

The use of initial capital letters in some terms, is another matter worth looking into. There is no problem with proper nouns, e.g. Naperian logarithms, but there can be fine discriminations, especially within groups. For instance, if 'HM Government' is to be used, a decision would have to be made about associated terms such as 'member of parliament', 'chief whip', etc.

Sometimes initial capital letters are used to indicate that a term should be interpreted strictly as defined in the document (e.g. 'Critical Power-unit', which is defined as the power-unit critical for the case under consideration). Obviously, such a practice would have to be advised in the document at the earliest possible stage.

Where existing publications, to which a consistency list has been applied, are taken over, care should be taken to establish the full effects of any proposed changes to the consistency list. For instance, some of the documents may be in loose chapter form, wherein chapters are revised, and when distributed supersede the current chapters. Also chapters may be reprinted for stock for subsequent sale to new subscribers. Should a new version of an old term or a spelling (e.g. substitution of 's' for 'z') be incorporated, not only would a revised chapter be inconsistent all the time the others remained unchanged, but those chapters which were reprinted for stock would be different from those currently held by subscribers. The time it may take to achieve complete consistency and the expense (e.g. resetting of type with its attendant procedures) of such changes would have to be taken into account when making a decision.

EDITORIAL TERMS OF REFERENCE FOR A PARTICULAR JOB

Prior to commencement of the actual work of editing, the editor should apprise himself of the criteria which should have been taken into account by the author during the preparation of the document. Where a document has been subjected to extensive revision in the course of its preparation, the wording of amendments suggested by commentators (who are not necessarily skilled communicators) may not have taken account of the original criteria, especially in respect of the standard of knowledge to be assumed for the reader.

The following are some questions which may need to be asked about the document.

- How important is it?
- Is it intended to command, suggest, advise or entice?
- For whom is it intended?
- What standard of English vocabulary has been assumed for the reader?
- What standard of technical knowledge has been assumed for the reader?

Depending on the editor's relationship with the author, and whether or not the editor has additional responsibilities within an organization, the following may also be appropriate.

- How is it to be presented? Binding? Typography?
- Is it to form part of a series, or is it just one-off?

EDITOR'S TECHNICAL KNOWLEDGE

With any document, the editor may be looked upon as an agent, acting not only for the author (to enhance his exposition) but also for the reader (to improve his understanding). As communication is the most important factor, the reader must, perforce, be the editor's main concern. Therefore, as the author and his collaborators are usually specialists and authorities, and the reader is unlikely to be either, it is more important that the editor should be able to follow the author's exposition against a background of broad general knowledge, rather than to act as another 'technical' referee, against a background of specialist knowledge.

Specialists can communicate with each other using a limited vocabulary, without the need to explain each term or idea as it is introduced. As an example the noun 'cat' has the following meanings: 'a small carnivorous animal of the genus felis, with short jaws, sharp teeth and soft fur: *zoological* – any species of the genus felis: *figurative* – a spiteful woman: *nautical* – a type of single-masted sailing boat; strong tackle or gear for drawing up the anchor to the cathead; cat o'nine tails; a double tripod . . .'

One marine specialist could safely assume that a fellow marine specialist would know which meaning of 'cat' was intended. Thus 'cat' is a form of shorthand, used between specialists to convey a particular image, and it is the editor's duty to ensure that the level of knowledge assumed for the reader is kept well in mind, and any such 'shorthand' is adequately defined or explained for his benefit.

Although specialist knowledge is not a prerequisite for editing, it is, nevertheless, essential for the editor to have a broad enough understanding of the subject, combined with a sufficiently wide general technical knowledge, to be able to recognize obvious mistakes and weak links in the exposition. Where the editor is compelled to work on a document which contains material about which he knows little or nothing, but which the projected reader would be expected to know about (such as the text of a lecture to a learned society) he may very often be able to acquire sufficient background knowledge on his weak subjects, e.g. computers, by selective readings from books in the local library. Where speed of assimilation is of the essence, books on technical matters, but written for children, can be very useful. These have the advantage that the level of assumed readership is such that simplicity of expression and lack of complicated technical detail are the criteria; which is ideal where a broad background knowledge is being sought in a hurry.

The editor should have a knowledge of mathematical notation and conventions, and should be able to recognize and distinguish between the various units used in physics and mechanics (e.g. to know that there is a difference between $kg\,m^2$ and kg/m^2).

The knowledge outlined in the preceding paragraphs will be of little use unless it is allied to a good store of common sense, a feeling for logic and a complete lack of self-deception. An editor can rarely expect to match the author's knowledge on every subject he is called upon to deal with, but by applying his own particular skills to complement those of the author he will ensure that the projected reader will be fairly treated. After all, the editor would not be expected, unless asked, to check the mathematics or the facts put forward by the author. If the author should state that the boiling point of water is 212 deg C, then this should be noted and pointed out by the editor, but were the author to say that the boiling point of water is 84 deg C at a particular altitude, this would need to be taken as read.

Referring again to the 212 deg C boiling point, it is surprising how a glaring error can be perpetuated from draft to draft; presumably on the assumption that it is so obvious that it will automatically correct itself. It is best to note all errors, however obvious or trivial they may appear to be, and *put them forward* for correction.

It can, of course, take years to accumulate a store of general and background knowledge in even one field, therefore, an editor should not be expected to be self-sufficient at an early stage in his career. He should, normally, be given the benefit of assistance and advice from more experienced colleagues for some time before being expected to work more or less on his own.

It is better to know where to find facts and figures, rather than to try to memorize them. A feel for the rightness of things, coupled with a willingness to look things up, should prove adequate. Facts or figures should never be altered without the knowledge of the author.

MAKING A START (THE FIRST READ THROUGH)

To facilitate work, it is as well to have two good single-sided copies of the manuscript; one for the editor's personal use, the other for preparation of a revised version, subsequent to discussions with the author, to enable the preparation of the manuscript required for the next stage of production (*see* Chapter 8). For a really 'difficult' document, a further copy may be necessary during the familiarization stage, to enable the editor to 'think aloud' by writing at random on the document while trying to absorb its contents.

The editor should refresh his memory on the author's specification, and his own terms of reference in relation to the document.

The first read through should, ideally, be completed without long intervals between sessions. This not only helps to maintain concentration, but also to more readily recall what has gone before (especially useful where such matters as logic and consistency of expression are important).

Although during the first read through obvious spelling and grammatical errors may be marked for future attention, no detailed editing should be attempted at this stage. Seeming errors, obscurities, ambiguities, gaps in reasoning, unexplained statements and suchlike, should be identified by a brief marginal note for study and resolution later.

At this stage, all effort should be directed at becoming familiar with the contents of the document, and trying to understand the author's intentions, even if they do not appear at first sight to have been realized. After a while the editor should get a feel for the document, and begin to form opinions on its merits as a means of communication, e.g. logical progress from A to Z, in a reasonable sequence.

Separate note should be made of the location of the first and subsequent appearances of any special terms, together with any apparent synonyms or variation thereof. This is important not only for consistency, but also for dealing with the vexed question of the use of initial capital letters, in some terms. Elegant variation, although not unacceptable in technical writing, is best discouraged for special terms. There is ample opportunity to display a vocabulary in the general text, but technically a 'spade' is best referred to as a 'spade' throughout. The separate note of location can facilitate examination of all the different locations as a group, with a consequent greater possibility of consistency being achieved.

With lengthy documents a 'skeleton' can sometimes be of help in visualizing the overall picture. Very often a list of paragraph headings alone can provide a good enough picture. It is helpful to have main headings in capitals, and subsidiary headings with just initial capitals. If there is a general lack of paragraph headings, it may be helpful to prepare some on the way through, not only for the editor's own assistance (and reassurance that he has understood well enough to précis the contents into headings) but also with a view to persuading the author to adopt some in order to assist the reader. The skeleton also enables the editor to speed up reference backwards and forwards, when he finds things which are puzzling or which 'ring a faint bell' during the early reading. It can, of course, be used during the next stage of editing, where relevance to the professed subject matter has to be tested.

PREPARING FOR DISCUSSIONS WITH THE AUTHOR

With the first read through and familiarization completed, the work of preparing a definitive list of queries for discussion with the author has to be started. At this stage the editor's concentration must be absolute, as, except where otherwise agreed (e.g. for a very complicated document) more than one bite at the editorial cherry is neither justified nor likely to be tolerated.

Genius has been defined as 'an infinite capacity for taking pains'. This definition could equally well be applied to editing. When all is said and done, the finished article can only be as good as the workmanship put into its preparation, and with editing, 'taking pains' is, perhaps, the most important ingredient, with enthusiasm and optimism following close behind.

Before commencing, the editor should decide on his form of note-taking and suggestions for rewording. Notes and suggested rewordings can be written directly on to the text, or can be written on a separate sheet and related to the text by a page number and marginal mark. If the editor's copy of the text is to be looked at by the author during the consultations, then it may be advisable to leave it virtually unmarked. There is a great temptation for an author to get excited if he sees his text heavily annotated, also his attention may be diverted from the point in question while he is puzzling out the 'sense' of the editor's comments lower down the page.

Pages should be clearly numbered to facilitate discussion at subsequent stages (which could be by post or by telephone).

The editor now has the following objectives:

(a) He must ensure that his and the author's terms of reference or specification are honoured.
(b) He must ensure that the document is an effective means of communication *at the level intended.*

He has, therefore, to put himself into the requisite frame of mind and maintain it until the task is complete.

With the projected reader firmly in mind, the document should now be subjected to the closest scrutiny. Each paragraph, and each sentence within it, should be read at least twice before passing to the next, firstly, to test the relevance of the material both to the subject as a whole, and in relation to its place in the structure of the document, and secondly, to test the acceptability of the wording as a means of communication at the level intended.

The technique of reading first to test the relevance and then again to test the acceptability of wording, can lose some of its effectiveness where presentation is sufficiently poor to warrant proposing extensive re-presentation. Very often the editor may see re-presentation as the only way to dispose of his queries. However, it is not advisable to base note-taking on the assumption that re-presentation will be accepted, and note-taking should, therefore, continue on the assumption that the structure of the document will remain substantially unchanged.

Relevance of Material and Structure of Document
Having familiarized himself with the document, and noted his points for further study, the editor should have a fairly good idea where presentation and the logic of the presentation are weak. Accordingly, he should now retain and expand those of his preliminary brief notes which he wishes to pursue, and prepare any new ones which may arise from this more concentrated study. The following are questions which he could ask himself (the 'skeleton' referred to in the preceding section can be helpful).

(a) Is each section (or main paragraph) within the scope of the subject of the document, and is it logically related to the structure of the document as a whole?
(b) Is the paragraph in question appropriate to its section?
(c) Are all the paragraphs within the section logically related each to the other?
(d) Are headings correctly related to subject matter, useful and sufficient in number?
(e) Is there any duplication of section headings or paragraph headings within each section?

Acceptability of Wording
The second reading, to establish if there are any queries which need to be discussed with the author, should cover the following: grammar, syntax, vocabulary, clarity, level of technical knowledge assumed for the reader and logic of exposition. It is not suggested that these items be considered separately, but they should be constantly at the front of the editor's mind.

Grammar and Syntax
The grammatical structure of the paragraph, and the sentences within it, should conform to good English usage; the fact that a document is 'technical' is no excuse for slovenliness. What constitutes good English usage depends very much on the editor's schooling and subsequent reading. However, if he cannot distinguish good from bad he should not be editing in the first place.

Obviously it is not possible to 'teach' grammar in a book such as this, but the bare necessities may be expressed as follows:

(a) Every sentence must have a subject (expressed or understood) and a finite verb (the predicate), e.g. *Men* (subject) *Work* (predicate). The term 'predicate' is also used to denote not only the verb, but also the verb together with its object, and the extension of its object.

(b) A finite verb is one which agrees with its subject in person and number, e.g. *Men* (they) *work*, not *Men* (he) *works*.

(c) The subject of the sentence must always be clear, especially when pronouns such as 'it' are introduced.

These simple rules have particular bearing on clarity and logic of exposition.

Often in technical documents recourse is made to tabulation, where a verb in a preamble governs a series of succeeding phrases. In such cases, care should be taken that the preamble does, in fact, correctly combine with each phrase. For example:

'Motor cars, on loan to personnel, shall not

(a) be cleaned in the car park,
(b) be driven by anyone but the named person,
(c) be left unlocked when unattended.'

Where the dependent phrases are not simple, single thoughts, this form of presentation can become awkward, especially in respect of punctuation, and the possible resultant necessity to use initial capital letters for each phrase.

Also in tabulation, care has to be taken that the sub-paragraphs follow the preamble in the same voice, mood or tense of the verb. The active or passive voice should be maintained, and there should be no switching between the indicative and imperative moods. Some examples of the pitfalls of tabulation are given in the appendix to this chapter.

Vocabulary   The language used should be that which can be readily understood by the projected reader, with reference to a dictionary being necessary only on very rare occasions.

Although lacking the detail of its bigger brothers, the *Concise Oxford Dictionary* may safely be taken as a guide to the words and their definitions which can be used in technical writing. Being constantly in print, it can also be assumed to be accessible to the average reader.

Care should be taken to question unnecessarily erudite synonyms (especially those which may be enjoying a current vogue). There is no sense in using a synonym, especially one which needs to be looked up in a dictionary, if there is a word in general use which serves the purpose equally well.

Discretion should be used in asking for technical terms to be explained or defined. It should not be assumed that every reader will have access to the appropriate glossaries. Where a term is critical for understanding, it is best to ask for an explanation to be included in the text the first time it appears; a small illustration may sometimes be helpful, even though it may add to costs.

It is as well to remember that every time the reader has to stop to check on a meaning, he is demonstrating the failure of the author and editor to gauge his knowledge. Language varies, of course, with the projected readership. The American magazine *Variety*, being sure of the vocabulary of its readers, specialized in condensed, snappy headlines. It once appeared with the classic headline 'Sticks Nix Hicks Pix', an indication to the readership that people who live in the suburbs do not care for films about country folk! When in doubt a 'Sticks Nix Hicks Pix' test could be applied. Generally, tests with a humorous connotation tend to stay in the mind. The old schoolboy howler 'Bedstead wanted by a Lady with brass knobs on' speaks as eloquently as any textbook on grammar. A few, less serious, examples of how not to do it are given at the end of the appendix to this chapter.

Clarity   Although grammar and language may be acceptable, the text may still be difficult to follow, and the meaning may be obscure. Unless the object is to impress with the extent of the author's erudition, simplicity should always be the keynote. The level of knowledge of the projected reader must again be the criterion for simplification. Whenever there is doubt, the following questions may be asked:

(a)   Is there another form of words better suited to the context?
(b)   Is it possible to make a clearer statement?
(c)   Can the text be made easier to read?

Where meaning is not clear, the editor should persist in his study of the text until he is able to deduce what the author is trying to say. He should then be able to suggest a rewording, pitched at the right level. At times, this can demand a great deal of effort on the part of the editor, but it is necessary, if only to obviate the need for premature and piecemeal consultations with the author. By worrying the text in private until it yields up its secrets, the editor has the advantage of being able to sleep on his proposed rewording, with the benefit of second thoughts, rather than having to make snap decisions at the time of consultation with the author. Another disadvantage of having the author clarify his own wording is that sometimes he will appear to justify it as it stands, which could place the editor in a quandary; he may feel that he was excessively obtuse in the first place, and that rewording is no longer necessary. Normally, if wording has taken a lot of effort to understand, it needs to be revised.

Graphs and Illustrations   Particular attention should be paid to graphs and illustrations which, for some strange reason, are often assumed to be sacrosanct, with any scrutiny by the editor deemed presumptuous.

With graphs, the most common complaint is that they can contain too much information at one time. Without recourse to colour, the different curves have to be identified by various patterns of broken lines, which can become very difficult to separate when too many of them are grouped together. It is no use expecting the reader to discriminate between a curve made up of 1 inch lines broken by dots, and another with 1¼ inch lines broken by dots. Other points to check are that a graph does not duplicate information already presented in a table in the same document, that the units for the axes are indicated and that any legends or captions are positively linked to the appropriate curves. The possibility that the information may be better presented in tabular form should also be considered.

With illustrations, the prime question to be asked is whether the illustration serves any useful purpose. It may be true that one picture can save a thousand words, but it is no good an author sprinkling drawings over his draft unless each one serves an essential purpose. Illustrations must complement or amplify the text. A plain cylinder with sealed ends, labelled 'Typical Frequency-wild Generator' should receive more than a perfunctory scrutiny before being passed unchallenged.

Other points which should be covered are as follows:

(a) Is the drawing (probably the author's rough) completely unambiguous, i.e. will the illustrator interpret it in an identical manner?

(b) Are all the necessary parts clearly labelled?

(c) Is the nomenclature in the labelling identical to the nomenclature in the corresponding text? If not, why not?

(d) Can the illustration be seen to be practical, e.g. if it is a mechanical control system does it have a realistic linkage?

Some further points on clarity and compatability with text are illustrated in the appendix to this chapter.

Reader's Technical Knowledge   In addition to an accurate assessment of the reader's technical knowledge, account may also have to be taken of language difficulties, and varying degrees of association with the subjects in question. A reader brought up from an early age surrounded by mechanical and electronic devices is more likely to have an inbred feel for technical subjects than one brought up in a predominately agrarian environment, even though technical schooling may be to a similar standard. Therefore, care should be taken before assuming that something is common knowledge. It is best to remember the maxim 'when in doubt spell it out'. Although this may possibly annoy some readers, it is a chance well worth taking.

Logic of Exposition   Statements such as 'thus', 'therefore', 'as has been shown', 'obviously', etc., should always be challenged, and seen to be substantiated by the preceding text. Where not substantiated by preceding text, a forward-looking cross-reference may be acceptable, depending on the context, e.g. where an explanation essential to text appearing later in the paper would lose its force if given earlier. Often such sweeping statements as those above can carry so much conviction that they may be passed by unchallenged. The editor must be convinced that the statement is true, and even in apparently obvious cases, it is best to make sure, rather than chance a weak link in the chain of reasoning. One false link in a logical chain can undermine the credibility of the whole document.

Editor's Note-taking   Unless an early appointment has been made for discussions with the author, the editor should ensure that his notes are sufficiently detailed to bring him quickly and accurately to the point at a later date. Hesitation on the part of the editor while trying to recall a point will usually mitigate against it when it finally comes to mind. The author may well consider that text which conceals a point so difficult to recall needs no revision. Care should also be taken to have any reference documents well flagged. Where necessary, the text to be quoted from reference documents should be marked. He who hesitates may well be lost!

DISCUSSIONS WITH THE AUTHOR

It is essential that the author's feelings be kept well in mind. He may feel that he has produced his document after going through what is to him a tedious process of drafting, consultation and agreement; often with commentators and referees with whom he has little rapport, and who, in turn, may not have been too tactful in expressing their opinions. Another point to be borne in mind, is that the author may have 'borrowed' text from other sources, some of which may be at, or outside, the limit of his own knowledge, and has, perforce, been taken by him on trust. Should the borrowed wording (which may well have been the best possible) have undergone change during the drafting and consultation stages, the author's response to editorial suggestions may, understandably, be inhibited.

The possibility of having to refer back on any matter will probably not be a pleasant prospect for the author to contemplate, not only because of the implied inefficiency, but also because he may see himself as caught up in a loop of tedious argument from which there is little chance of early escape. With his spirits probably at low ebb, it needs a Henry V to re-kindle his enthusiasm and inspire him 'once more unto the breach', and this is an important part of the editor's task.

After all the effort leading up to the meeting with the author, it is imperative that its value is not lessened by holding the discussions in any but the best possible surroundings and atmosphere.

It is essential that the author should not appear to lose face, or be forced into a schoolmaster/pupil relationship (although it would be nice if some lessons were learned on both sides). The editor's work must complement the author's work, and as the author should not try to be 'clever' neither should the editor.

Consultations are more likely to be successful (and painless) if two conditions are met. First, the discussions should be held away from the telephone and in uninterrupted privacy. This ensures the absence of eavesdroppers, who, apparently, even with the best of intentions, cannot ignore the discussions, and are sometimes so pushed past the bounds of discretion that they have to interfere. The presence of such third parties would probably put the author on the defensive, and make him try that much harder to avoid having to climb down. Second, the discussions should be confidential between the author and the editor.

It is best to start by complimenting the author, if this is at all justified. Any 'broad' worries should be mentioned before getting down to detail. It is essential to maintain a sense of proportion, and a careful watch should be kept on any tension which may build up. After all, it is very unlikely that there will be a complete absence of serious differences of opinion. Good humour allied to a change of subject, away from the work in hand, or a break for tea or coffee, should normally see a lowering of temperature.

Following the discussions, the editor should, wherever practicable, insist on preparing the revised version to be sent to the author for agreement. It is not wise to agree that the author should prepare the revision, as he may retract some of his agreements, or make amendments which will unwittingly spoil the logical sequence of the document, or introduce inconsistencies. The revisions should be shown in manuscript, or as separate pieces of typescript, on the draft which was discussed, so that changes may be readily identified; and, as with the discussions, the revised document should, unless otherwise agreed, be confidential between the author and the editor. Methods for preparing revised versions of drafts are discussed more fully in Chapter 8.

Depending on the intended use of the document, it may be possible to leave the author to decide whether or not he wishes to acknowledge the editor's contribution. This may seem a little hard to a publicity-conscious editor, but it does go a long way towards building up a good relationship with 'clients'. After all, communication is the object, and its achievement should be sufficient reward. Normally, it soon becomes known that the editor 'knows his stuff' or 'is OK', and this, of course, makes his life a lot easier in the future.

USEFUL PUBLICATIONS FOR THE EDITOR

- *Concise Oxford Dictionary*
- National Physical Laboratory booklet *Changing to the Metric System*
- A technical dictionary, such as *Chambers*
- British Standards (*see* Chapter 10)

APPENDIX: EXAMPLES

DELEGATED POWERS

Ideally, the editor-in-chief should also be the head of the department responsible for satisfying the printing requirements of an organization. As he will probably be the most experienced of the publications staff, he will then be able to exert his influence at all stages in the preparation and production of publications.

The following are examples of some of the responsibilities which management could delegate to the head of such a department.

(a) Ensuring that before a document is reproduced all editorial processes have been completed.

(b) Monitoring and advising management on the reproduction and printing work in the organization.

(c) Advising on, and where necessary, controlling costs.

(d) Protecting the corporate image as projected by publications.

(e) Acting as agent for all reproduction and printing work within the organization.

(f) Advising on methods of conveying information so as to achieve optimum cost-effectiveness and economy of effort at all stages of preparation and publication.

(g) Ensuring that design, layout and typography conform to house rules, and laying down such rules, where necessary.

(h) Deciding on the method of reproduction (photocopying, photo lithography, etc.).

(j) Controlling the preparation and processing of illustrations, printer's copy, proofs, camera copy.

(k) Deciding on time-scales and priorities.

(l) Advising on the suitability of text as a means of communication.

(m) Advising on inconsistencies with related or associated documentation.

(n) Deciding in consultation with the originator on the degree of editing, and the degree of reference back to the originator.

An editor without any other responsibilities in an organization would need, at least, the powers set out in (d), (l), (m), (n) and perhaps (f). Where the editor is freelance, (l), (m) and (n) and possibly (k) would need to be agreed with the 'client'.

PITFALLS OF TABULATION

One type of mistake which can be introduced is illustrated below –

'A significant improvement can be achieved by making personnel aware of the potential danger areas, and laying down improved general handling practices, such as:

(a) Not removing or replacing . . .
(b) Not unnecessarily touching the . . .
(c) By using . . .
(d) Particular attention should be given to . . .'

Obviously (c) should read 'Using . . .' and (d) should read 'Paying particular attention to . . .'

Another type of mistake is the change of mood and voice, as illustrated below –

'Following re-assembly:

(a) Tighten and lock all joints.
(b) The plug leads should be positioned . . .
(c) Check that . . .
(d) Care should be taken that all points of attachment . . .'

To achieve uniformity either (a) and (c) or (b) and (d) should be reworded.

A problem arises with the tabulation shown in the chapter (*see* page 108) where anything but a single simple phrase follows the preamble. Suppose instead of –

'Motor cars, on loan to personnel, shall not

(a) be cleaned in the car park,
(b) be driven by anyone but the named person,
(c) be left unlocked when unattended.'

one of the phrases were to be qualified by an additional clause on the following lines –

'Motor cars, on loan to personnel, shall not

(a) be cleaned in the car park,
(b) be driven by anyone but the named person. *Where for the purpose of repair or servicing, it is necessary for another person to drive the car, agreement should be obtained from the Transport Manager.*
(c) be left unlocked when unattended.'

then the insertion of a complete sentence at the end of (b) with its initial capital and full stop will jar with the lower case/comma layout of (a) and the lower case/stop layout of (c), and will necessitate a change of presentation to enable (a), (b) and (c) each to start with an initial capital and end with a full stop. There are a few solutions, but with the new presentation 'shall not' would have to appear at the beginning of (a), (b) and (c) and the preamble would have to be reworded to allow (a), (b) and (c) to stand on their own. The revised version could be on the following lines.

'The following rules apply to motor cars on loan to personnel.

(a) They shall not be cleaned in the car park.
(b) They shall not be driven . . . person. Where . . . Transport Manager.
(c) They shall not be left unlocked when unattended.'

In conclusion, tabulated presentations should be treated with caution, and when in doubt, the preamble and its punctuation should be read through with each dependent phrase or clause and their punctuations in turn, to establish that the sentences are grammatically complete, and the punctuation, taken as a whole, is conventional.

CLARITY OF AUTHOR'S 'ROUGH' AND COMPATABILITY WITH TEXT

Comparison of a figure with its complementary text can often lead to questions and suggestions, in addition to those on the text alone. The following text and figure are of this type.

MOS device construction

In an electronic circuit, a metal-oxide semi-conductor (MOS)
2 device appears as a voltage-controlled resistor in which the equivalent MOS resistance between the drain and source is
4 varied by a voltage applied to the gate electrode (*see* Figure 5.1). Physically, the gate electrode is a thin layer of metal deposited on
6 a very thin layer of silicon dioxide (S_iO_2 (glass)), typically 1000 to 14000 Ångstroms thick. This layer of glass effectively insulates
8 the gate from the substrate, in essence, forming a capacitor whose plates are the gate and substrate with the dielectric being the layer
10 of S_iO_2 between the gate and substrate.

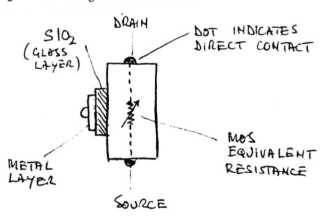

Fig. 5.1   Typical MOS device showing the insulated gate.

At this early stage, the text and figure should match precisely, otherwise there could be subsequent uncertainty and annoyance.

Remembering that the editor is protecting the reader's interests, the notes for the discussion with the author could be on the following lines:

Line 2: 'appears', prefer 'functions' or 'serves as'.
Line 3: Is 'MOS' necessary?
Line 4: Where is the 'gate electrode' on the figure?
Line 6: Silicon is Si not 'S_i'.
Line 7: 'Ångstroms' – should this be 'Ångstrom Units'?. Also should there be a conversion factor e.g.

one micron = 10,000 Ångstrom Units, or 1 Å. = 3.937×10^{-9} inch?

Line 8: Is 'the gate' the 'gate electrode'?
Line 8/9: 'Whose plates are' – to avoid personification, suggest 'the plates of which are'.
Line 9 : Is 'the gate' the 'gate electrode'.
Line 10: 'S_iO_2' – see previous *re* silicon – prefer 'glass'.
Line 10: Is 'the gate' the 'gate electrode'?

In the figure –

What does 'DOT INDICATES DIRECT CONTACT' mean in relation to text?
Should the 'substrate' – see line 8 – be indicated?
Qualify and identify 'GATE' in light of queries on text.
Compare the relative thickness of the glass and metal layers with the text, where in line 5/6 'thin layer of metal . . . very thin layer of silicon . . .'.
Should there be an indication of actual size of the device?

READER'S TECHNICAL KNOWLEDGE

The author's wording, very early in the draft, was as follows:

> The term 'screening' may be defined as the absorption of electric energy which is radiated by a current flow. A metal screen, in the form of metallic braiding, or a cable harness, surrounds the cables that form the ignition high tension system and carries the radiated electrical energy to earth, so preventing electrical interference with the aircraft radio equipment. In addition, a harness protects the ignition cables from physical damage and deterioration and, if water-proofed, prevents the ingress of fluids, it also minimizes the risk of fire.

The editor considered that, at this early stage, a more fundamental approach would better prepare the reader for what was to follow. Accordingly, the following rewording was put forward for discussion:

> The passage of high tension current along the ignition cables from the magnetos to the sparking plugs results in unwanted electrical radiation which could, if not checked, result in interference with other aircraft equipment such as radio. Avoidance of interference is achieved by 'screening' the ignition cables by covering them with a metallic braiding which is connected to earth. It is also necessary to provide protection against mechanical damage, deterioration and contact with liquids, and this is normally achieved either by enclosing the cables in a prefabricated 'ignition harness' or by providing an outer covering of neoprene or plastics tubing.

LOGIC OF EXPOSITION

The author's draft was as follows:

7 Safety Precautions

7.1 *General*   The provisioning of a static free work station will not, on its own, ensure that no static sensitive devices will be destroyed. In order to achieve this certain standard operating and handling procedures should be adhered to, thus ensuring complete effectiveness of the facility.

7.1.1 Engineers should be static conscious and consider electro-static damage avoidance as an engineering parameter when conducting maintenance and repairs, and be aware of the necessity for the elimination of such notorious static generators as plastic envelopes, non-conductive tapes and other plastics, nylon and rubber paraphernalia.

Although there are no actual errors of fact, some statements were considered to be rather sweeping, and others unnecessarily restrictive. Accordingly, the following rewording was suggested by the editor.

7 Additional Precautions ('safety' has implications of personal welfare)

7.1 *General*   The provisioning of an electro-static-free work station will not, on its own, ensure that no electro-static-sensitive devices will be damaged or destroyed. Complete protection may only be achieved when certain standard operating and handling procedures are also adhered to. Only then will the complete effectiveness of the work station be realized.

7.1.1 Persons engaged in maintenance or repair work should be electro-static conscious, and should consider the avoidance of damage by electro-static charges as a normal responsibility. They should also be aware of the necessity for the elimination of electro-static generators such as plastics envelopes, non-conductive tapes and other commonly used items made from plastics, nylon and rubber.

AWFUL REMINDERS

No apologies are made for the following; they are just awful reminders. When one of them slips through your net, take heed of the words of Ella Wheeler Wilcox – 'Laugh and the world laughs with you, weep and you weep alone' – and take comfort that it could, perhaps, have been worse.

'I have shot mine arrow o'er the house, and hurt my brother.' (Hamlet)

TRAFFIC WARDEN SHOT IN VERMIN HUNT (Newspaper headline)

Having been carried out successfully on each of four occasions by Mr Jones, the process may now be considered to be foolproof. (Report to Board of Directors)

'My boy don't know the meaning of the word "fear"' (Boxer's Manager)

The most common cause of cramp under the ribs on the right side (so called stitch in the side) which occurs in runners or other athletes is a spasm of the transverse colon and the hepatic flexure. The spastic contraction may be prolonged, causing a relative ischemia of the vessels of the mesentery and producing the characteristic pain. (Extract from a medical journal reproduced in a lay sports magazine. The dictionary was not much help either.)

I Hate Definitions (Benjamin Disraeli)

A major modification is one having a significant effect on the airworthiness of the aeroplane, or on the scheduled data or limitations associated with it. (What was intended was '. . . is one which requires design investigation to establish that it does not have a significant adverse effect . . .' The 'or' phrases also need tidying up.)

Proof Readers' Rule! OJ? (Graffiti)

Men formed a chain and tried to light the fire with buckets of water. (Newspaper report)

A dense fox the night before did not augur well for the first meeting of the . . . Hunt. (Newspaper report)

The Simple Adjective Gives Little Trouble (English textbook)

WANTED – man and woman to tend two horses, both Protestant. (Advertisement)

Neither Do Adverbs

The bride and groom left for Eastbourne where their honeymoon will be spent amid a shower of confetti. (Newspaper report)

The Dreaded 'It'

When the baby has finished its bottle drop it in a saucepan and boil it. (Magazine Article)

'We are all thrilled at winning the Cup', said the Club Manager, 'and when the lads have had their bath we shall all have a drink out of it.' (Newspaper report)

'We must speak by the card, or equivocation will undo us.' (Hamlet)

It is now quite clear that, having regard to all or many of the circumstances obtaining, and making allowance for the potential factors which form an integral part of the question, viewed in whatever light, no clear-cut decision can be attempted until a more exhaustive probing of the overall position has resulted in some elucidation of every aspect, resulting in the possibility of an understanding being reached as to what exactly it is that is being considered. (Loose minute)

CHECK LIST

As editing is more of an art than a science, a check list may seem out of place. However, when the editor has prepared the revised version of the document, he may wish to set his mind at rest before sending the document to the author. The following, read in conjunction with the procedures and check lists in Chapter 8, should ensure that most of the ground is covered.

Editor's Check List

- Is the title of the document still acceptable?
- Does the summary need revision?
- Are the terms of the author's specification still met? (*see* page 106)
- Has consistency been maintained? (*see* page 102)
- Is there a need for a special section on terms?
- Is the structure of the document and the interrelation of paragraphs still acceptable? (*see* page 107)
- Are the section and paragraph titles still acceptable? (*see* page 107)
- Is the wording still at an acceptable level? (*see* pages 107–9)
- Are the graphs, illustrations and tables still correctly related to the text? (*see* page 109)
- Have all new 'thus' and 'therefore' clauses been tested? (*see* page 110)
- Are there any parts of the mathematical notation which necessitate special instructions?

The editor's own method of working, and the allocation of editorial responsibilities within his own organization (*see* Chapter 8) will, no doubt, be the factors which will determine the scope of any check list.

CHAPTER 6

Planning and Commissioning Technical Translations

إعـداد الترجمــات الفنيــة

PLANNING ET MISE EN ROUTE DE TRADUCTIONS TECHNIQUES

PLANUNG UND KOMMISSIONIERUNG DER FACHÜBERSETZUNGEN

ПЛАНИРОВАНИЕ И ВЫПОЛНЕНИЕ ТЕХНИЧЕСКИХ ПЕРЕВОДОВ

by
DENIS W. F. TYSON

Purchasers of mass-produced imported items such as cameras, tape recorders and hair dryers may occasionally be astonished, amused, frustrated or even incensed by the accompanying instructional material that appears to take the English language beyond the limits of sensible comprehension. Such products, of course, are not sold on the quality of their supporting literature. Nevertheless, they can serve as an object lesson on the kind of anomalies that can be introduced into written technical information, through the medium of translation, by someone who is not a natural speaker of the language concerned.

Capital equipment exporters must rely on the effectiveness of their technical literature as a product support tool that can save much valuable maintenance time, and local supervision. However, the preparation of technical information to cover such areas as: technical specifications, commissioning, operation, fault-finding, description, servicing, maintenance and software, is a time-consuming undertaking; and having assembled a set of publications in one language, a supplier may be unwilling to invest further by rewriting them in another. Fortunately, translation is less expensive, but if it is badly done it can totally undermine a supplier's credibility in the eyes of his customer.

Anyone likely to be concerned with commissioning translated technical information needs to be aware of the potential pitfalls and what may be done by way of ensuring that the individual at the translating interface is properly briefed and experienced for the task in hand. The total process is shown in Figure 6.1.

COMMUNICATING THROUGH TRANSLATION
用翻译来沟通

The words 'transfer' and 'translate' are linguistically closely related, and the transference of ideas from one language to another is the essence of a translator's skill. We often take for granted written material in our own

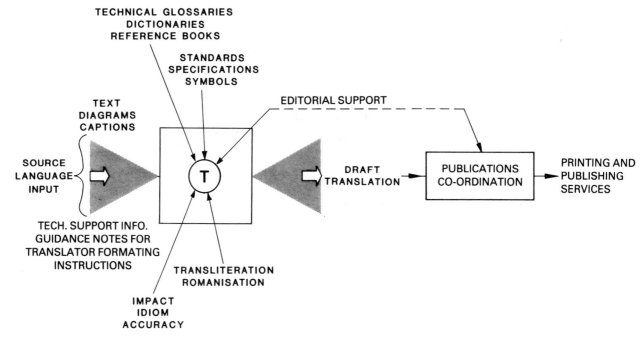

TECHNICAL GLOSSARIES
DICTIONARIES
REFERENCE BOOKS

STANDARDS
SPECIFICATIONS
SYMBOLS

EDITORIAL SUPPORT

TEXT
DIAGRAMS
CAPTIONS

SOURCE
LANGUAGE
INPUT

T

DRAFT
TRANSLATION

PUBLICATIONS
CO-ORDINATION

PRINTING AND
PUBLISHING
SERVICES

TECH. SUPPORT INFO.
GUIDANCE NOTES FOR
TRANSLATOR FORMATING
INSTRUCTIONS

TRANSLITERATION
ROMANISATION

IMPACT
IDIOM
ACCURACY

Fig. 6.1   The translation process.

language, by instantly accepting or rejecting it on its apparent merits, but not by dwelling on the finer grammatical points or clever choice of words! On the other hand, translation requires that the source language text be subjected to thoughtful and searching scrutiny in order to evolve a translated version containing the precise information content of the original. The translation has equally to be absorbed as a piece of natural reading by a foreign reader; this 'naturalness' is the ultimate measure of the talent exercised in its translation.

Translators, technical authors and editors share similar aspects of professional expertise; the translator, however, needs to exhibit the skills of all three. Each of these professionals accepts the given information at a technical level of understanding, then re-defines and presents it in a form suited to the requirements of intended readers. The first foreign recipient of a source language document is often a translator, whose primary qualification is the capability to appreciate and absorb its contents. The author's mantle falls to some extent on his shoulders, and it is to the translated version that foreign readers of the document turn for their 'source' information.

Although he possesses a bilingual understanding of both the source and the translated versions of technical material, a translator can disclaim responsibility for errors and omissions in the text presented to him. If the prime information is deficient, he will almost certainly lack the means, or the time needed to recognize it as such, let alone correct it. Complications arise when multi-language versions of a publication are commissioned. As secondary communicators, the individual translators may be led inadvertently into further ambiguity by erroneous facts supplied to them, and each may choose a slightly different misinterpretation of them.

Only authors who understand the language into which their text is to be translated can appreciate the various factors of style, compromise, terminology, distortion of meaning, omissions, emphasis, exactitude that might affect the quality of the translated version. The fact is that such superior knowledge may be absent, even to the extent that the author, or the person commissioning a translation may not recognize the material in its new form, or even know the direction in which it should be read! In such instances, the reliance placed on a translator is both onerous and total.

PREPARATION OF SOURCE LANGUAGE MATERIAL
Προετοιμασία γλωσσικοῦ ὑλικοῦ ἀπό πηγές

Technical information is not necessarily written with subsequent translation in mind. Written technical information normally requires a certain amount of revision prior to submission for translation. This final check can afford a useful opportunity for making last-minute adjustments and for aiding the translator.

In view of the widespread understanding of technical English, it can sometimes be sufficient to issue an alternative version for foreign readers, and translate only selected parts of the text, such as operating instructions, hazard warnings, etc. If a text contains special terminology, abbreviations and acronyms, then explanatory glossaries could be invaluable to the readers. The conversion of imperial measurements to metric should be handled by a technical author or engineer. Copies of similar translated material should be collated so as to assist the translator in his understanding of the subject. It is particularly important to ensure that the original copy is complete and inclusive of all supporting illustrations. Care should be taken to see that the documents submitted are easily decipherable, because nothing is more aggravating than having to pore over badly copied, faded, torn or otherwise illegible copy, and at the same time attempt to extract a coherent meaning from it.

The required form of presentation of translated material needs careful consideration and page formats or laymark sheets should be supplied to the translator. It goes almost without saying, that good technical writing and presentation practices are essential to accomplish effective communication, and that the source material is the bedrock upon which it is laid. The essential requirements are logical exposition, avoidance of unnecessary jargon, use of consistent terminology, accuracy, conciseness, ease of reference and a knowledge of the level of technical understanding of the intended readership.

SELECTING TRANSLATION SERVICES
翻 訳 サ ー ビ ス の 選 択 決 定

Translation agencies are the main source of reliably co-ordinated translation facilities, and it is obviously important to select a professional company with a sound reputation. Freelance translators are retained mostly by agencies, who match their specialities and experience to the client's needs. Some agencies can arrange for work to be performed in the target language country, and will offer direct contact between the translator and the client's overseas agent or distributor.

Two organizations that can supply help and advice to exporters or others wishing to communicate abroad are ASLIB, Association for Information Management, who can supply lists of specialist translators, and THE (Technical Help for Exporters). The Institute of Linguists, a learned society, maintains contacts between translation activities at home and abroad through its membership and its affiliated body of professional practitioners, the Translators Guild.

Special knowledge on the part of an agency can be advantageous, as works of reference do not always furnish acceptable descriptions in specialized fields of technology. Therefore, the technical experience of the translator in the use of trade terminology can make all the difference between his choosing an academically correct rendering, or using one couched in contemporary terminology, thereby affording greater verisimilitude and consequent ready acceptance by a discerning readership.

The estimated cost per one thousand words of translated material varies widely in accordance with the factors already noted. An estimate for translating a relatively non-specialized document into a European language such as German, French or Spanish could amount to only one third of that for the translation of a high-technology subject into, say, Arabic, Chinese or Russian, all of which require non-roman typesetting facilities.

Estimated prices for translation, whether low or high, may bear little obvious relationship to the finished product. The inclusion of supporting services needs to be borne in mind, for a simple estimate would probably only cover the preparation of a typed pre-publication draft. Special checking arrangements by independent translators, or a certification that the translation is true and accurate for legal considerations may be required. Other cost factors are the production deadline, the required format and length of document, liaison and co-ordination time, data storage facilities for future updating, indexing and artwork preparation, if only in the form of annotated overlays. (*See* Figure 6.2.)

COST PER 1000 WORDS DEPENDENT ON:

1 *SCOPE OF TRANSLATION*
   (a) Total
   (b) Selective
   (c) Abridged
   (d) Multi-lingual
2 *PLACE OF TRANSLATION*
   (a) In U.K.
   (b) Abroad

3 *SUBJECT SPECIALIZATION*
4 *TECHNICAL COMPLEXITY*
5 *NEED FOR LIAISON WITH EXPERTS*
6 *DEADLINE REQUIREMENT*

7 *TYPESETTING*
   (a) European roman
   (b) European non-roman
   (c) Non-European
        syllabaric
        pictographic

Fig. 6.2   Factors affecting translation costs

BRIEFING TRANSLATORS
Instrucciones para los traductores

It must be realized that translators are only earning while they are working, and as a result they may occasionally appear reluctant to enter into discussion with a client. If personal liaison is considered essential, it should be planned and allowed for in the initial brief and estimate. An agency has the right to insist on being addressed first on all matters requiring consultation, in order to protect its guarantees, its indemnity and terms of trade.

A brief on the background to the task and the intended use of the document can be useful. Where 'word-for-word' translation of advertising copy is inapposite, it can be highly desirable for the translator to have access to the client's overseas agent. Where repetitive material occurs, the translator's advice on how best to avoid unnecessary costs should be sought. Ensure that the deadline is known and agreed, and try to avoid last-minute changes to the copy. Sometimes there is a requirement for selective translation, a précis, or an abridged version. An experienced translator can undertake such re-formatting, but careful briefing by the person commissioning the task is essential.

CHECKING TRANSLATIONS
Kontroleren en redigeren van vertalingen

A perfect translation is a matter of subjective, and therefore disputable, opinion. A proper question to ask of a translator or agency is: 'What arrangements will be made to check the translation, and are final editorial facilities available?' Checking may be carried out at several levels – self-checking by the translator, a technical evaluation by an independent checker (best performed in the destined country of the recipients), editorial checks at the typesetting preparation stage, and a final proof-reading exercise prior to publication. An independent technical checker should be just as well qualified as the translator, since input from someone having a less capable grasp of the language, or subject, could prove more harmful than beneficial. At any event, no change should be made to translated copy without direct reference to its original translator.

One should appreciate that an author's style and choice of vocabulary can never be perfectly transposed into another language. Reference to the pages of a thesaurus will confirm that words may often be interchangeable without at the same time incurring or creating any noticeable change of meaning. A translator enjoys the privilege of selecting the appropriate equivalent vocabulary for the source language information in order to express it in his own language. Comparison of the renderings of two translators working on the same task invariably reveals that they do not select identical words or expressions. So, the job of a checker is not to attempt to rewrite a translation, but to ascertain that it faithfully reflects the content of the original, without distortion, omission or incorrect sequencing of information, and to remember that the source document is the sole standard against which the end-product should be assessed.

Reverse translations from the target back to the source language are rarely justifiable. However, when all, or part of, a translation is tape-recorded back to the source language, it enables the person who commissioned the translation to verify that the substance of the original contents has been covered. This is the only expedient way in which a non-linguist can participate in the checking process.

PUBLICATION PRESENTATION
Presentation av publikationen

Various methods of presenting translated material are possible, and an agency can give sound advice in this respect. Two of the more common methods are to present the translated version alongside the source information on a separate page, or interleaved on transparent overlays in distinctive colours. Items on drawings can be number-keyed, and the associated spare parts can appear suitably tabulated on adjacent spares lists.

Company names do not always lend themselves effectively to transliteration into another script. It can be important to retain names and addresses in the original source form as well as in the transliterated version.

It is important to ensure that typesetting is performed by a specialist foreign language typesetter, otherwise there will be a high risk of typographical errors slipping through owing to a lack of linguistic knowledge on the part of the setters.

'Page-for-page' translations are difficult to achieve without considerable paste-up ingenuity and expertise, and it is normally advisable to use a system of paragraph numbering when cross-referencing of material between languages is desired. It is worth mentioning here that Arabic publications read from right to left, so that the final page of an English book becomes the front page of its Arabic version. A variant on this theme is the presentation of a dual-language book having a second language printed on the reverse of every page, so that it can be read by turning the book about, and reading from the last page of the first language version to the front cover. Presentation possibilities are seemingly endless and any reasonable technique that serves to eliminate unnecessary translation costs or improve the final appearance of the work is worth considering.

MACHINE BASED AND DP (DATA PROCESSING) AIDS
Вспомогательные средства, основанные на ЭВМ

Automated means of information processing are now widely obtainable. Machines will not replace translators, any more than word processors have replaced typists, but they will certainly lighten their work load. Data bases or multi-lingual terminology banks are in the course of being formulated and tested; spelling checkers are available, and word processors have made an anachronism of repetitious manual typing. Some translation agencies offer OCR (optical character recognition) facilities. This enables specially typed copy from a translator who has no access to a word processor to be fed through a scanning device converting the characters into a computer-compatible code, to which a word processor or film setter will respond. This considerably improves and accelerates the pre-processing stages with a corresponding overall cost reduction. Facsimile services are available through the postal services for transmitting foreign language copy and its accompanying illustrations within the UK and abroad.

GENERAL OBSERVATIONS
Ĝeneralaj observoj

Technical authors and editors are not normally required to cultivate a working knowledge of foreign languages. It is possible to acquire a useful reading facility in several languages, adequate at least to be able to check over a finished translation by reference to the source language material, which may not necessarily be in English. Criticism of a translator's style and choice of words must rest with his peers, unless there are obvious inconsistencies between one part of a document and another. Useful though a minimal linguistic facility may undoubtedly be for a technical communicator, its acquisition is difficult, since language course sylla-buses are hardly ever dedicated to the specialized aspects of practising technology workers.

Finally, a word on film commentaries. The key is to select a profes-sionally experienced commentator, and to appreciate that voice and delivery are extremely important. Agencies can often arrange for suitable commentators to be commissioned. The English script should be sup-plied to the translator together with a copy of the original film, and his version should be supplied to the commentator for editing in order to compress or expand it, and to align it with the time frame of the film. Studio time is expensive, and it will help if the commentator is allowed to see the film prior to making the translated recording or 'voice-over'.

Technical translation is a highly developed profession, and standards are high. A first-rate service will be obtained from an established agency, and its effectiveness can be enhanced if the customer's representative has an informed appreciation of problems that may be encountered through genuine misunderstanding or inadequate preparation of the source mate-rial supplied.

APPENDIX: SIMPLIFIED INTERNATIONAL LANGUAGE – AN ALTERNATIVE TO TRANSLATION

To facilitate the provision of international product support documenta-tion there is an International Language for Servicing and Maintenance (ILSAM). The information on ILSAM was kindly provided by M & E White Consultants Ltd, 477 Reading Road, Winnersh, Wokingham, Berkshire RG11 5HX, who hold the world marketing rights for ILSAM. ILSAM improves communication between the writer and the user of technical information by providing a set of rules for:

(a) controlling the variety of words used;
(b) ensuring standardized grammatical constructions;
(c) ensuring that words have clearly defined meanings.

Standard English words are used throughout. The vocabulary com-prises about 800 words, those most used by service personnel. Few additional words are needed to adapt for a particular equipment field or for applications other than in servicing: i.e. commercial dealings. If the written material is to be translated into another language ILSAM has particular benefit in simplifying and standardizing the documents prior to translation. ILSAM was derived from Caterpillar Fundamental English (CFE) a development by the Caterpillar Company of America. Caterpillar publish some 20,000 technical publications and translate into 50 lan-guages to meet requirements of 10,000 agents and engineers. CFE resulted from a research and development programme in their service publications department where there was an expressed wish to co-ordinate, simplify and discipline publishing activities. The research programme was headed by Bernt W. von Glasenapp of the service training department who was not only a technical writer and editor but a linguist with a working knowledge of servicing in a number of countries.

Some of the reasons for the research being approved were as follows:

(a) The importance of service to support the Caterpillar image was realized.

(b) The role of service literature in protecting the investment by the user was known.

(c) The product line extended to 170 items making reliance on memory useless.

(d) The products were becoming more sophisticated.

(e) The ever-developing vocabulary was proving too complex for mechanics.

(f) Labour costs were rising, making accurate diagnosis essential before work was started.

THE CATERPILLAR DEVELOPMENT

The investigation began with a review of current practices and of the role of translation in communication. It was felt that translation gave rise to problems because advancing technology required constant development of new words in parts of the world not using technically-developed languages. Translation also tended to introduce technical errors and produced months of delay between the issue of the English version of a product manual and the foreign version. The wartime acceptance of English as a technical language for the world had not been maintained, and some countries were against the use of English to the point at which they would prefer translations (errors included). This led to research into the use of symbols as a common language, a method advocated by others in time past.

It was from these considerations that the first CFE concept appeared. This suggested a language of symbols but using English words as the symbols. This in turn demanded two things: first, that the symbols must have a unique meaning (one word – one meaning) and second, that the number of symbols used (or words used) should be minimized and thereafter strictly controlled.

This expresses quite clearly the CFE and ILSAM concepts – use of a restricted number of English words as symbols having (as far as possible) one clear meaning in their field of use. The next stage of research clearly demanded identification of these all-important words and this required investigation of the words used at that time in Caterpillar documents and of their frequency of appearance. At the same time the range of nouns used for product, parts, materials and tools nomenclature was reviewed.

Finally, the most used words and their synonyms were examined on a number of counts:

(a) Were the words best suited to the area of communication (i.e. service engineering)?

(b) Were the words suited to the product range (i.e. earthmovers)?

(c) Could the word meet the 'one word – one meaning' requirement?

(d) Was there an internationally preferred word (e.g. assist rather than help)?

(e) How much could the range of verbs be restricted?

At the same time duplication was avoided and 'English readability' considered. Eventually a vocabulary of some 800 words was agreed upon and a product nomenclature guide prepared listing and illustrating some 1,500 tools and parts for earthmoving plant. This nomenclature guide and the CFE dictionary were the two basic reference books for users of the CFE system. The opportunity for a review of writing practices was taken and a third book produced entitled *Writers Guide for CFE*. This identified some of the basic crimes in technical writing and presented a set of rules for improvements including: shortened sentences, step-by-step procedures, simplified constructions, consistency in use of nomenclature, no colloquialisms, etc. These rules were accepted without difficulty by Caterpillar authors and have contributed to effective communication wherever Caterpillar publications are used.

Caterpillar research indicated that technical writing time could be divided as follows: 60% research, 20% structure and 20% writing. The new writing techniques and the use of CFE resulted in some initial increase in the latter percentage, but this was a small part of the total time taken and the writing time soon returned to normal as CFE became a habit. Careful editing was of course necessary in the early days. In practice, writers tend to write their first draft quite freely and then convert to CFE at second drafting. One significant benefit has been a large reduction in writer training time; from three to six months down to a few days.

A text written in CFE or ILSAM has no distortion and only normal English words are used (*see* p. 129). The constraints imposed by the simplified construction, consistent nomenclature, restricted vocabulary and the writing rules combine to assist comprehension and to speed information retrieval – important features of effective communication. It is interesting to note that the introduction of CFE without notice in Caterpillar publications which were distributed worldwide produced no comments about strange constructions or reduced vocabulary. The language has proved to be completely acceptable to staff at all levels. The first tangible benefit was the reduction in the number of technical enquiries arising from misunderstandings or wrong interpretation of customer manuals.

Attention was then given to the question of training international users in the use of the new manuals and to the possibility of introducing English words as symbols. Tests were made in a number of countries and indicated that 800 symbols could be taught in a relatively short period; as short as 40 hours in some countries. A 30-lesson course was devised and instructor and student manuals prepared to support the training. The words were taught purely as symbols by an instructor speaking from both English and the language of the country of use. Within one year more than 2,500 student manuals and 280 instructor manuals had been issued and a pool of mechanics started having the additional qualification that, without speaking English, they could work directly from English language manuals written in CFE.

The Caterpillar Company were then able to curtail or terminate the issue of certain publications that were previously produced in a number of languages. The extent of the savings made may be obvious; what is less obvious, but has proved none the less important, is the improvement in communication and the reduction in errors and misunderstandings on technical points.

There has been general acceptance of the English words as symbols even in some countries expected to be hostile to the concept. One full year of testing in four continents proved the method beyond all doubt. Personnel in Europe, Scandinavia, Russia, Japan, South Africa, French-speaking Africa, South America, Spain, Portugal, Iceland and Libya have been trained. The increasing number of mechanics in the international labour pool who are able to work directly from an English text must prove of increasing interest to companies other than Caterpillar, and some companies having joint dealerships with Caterpillar may already see benefits.

THE NEED FOR TRANSLATION

However, there are still situations in which not all personnel are prepared to learn the 800 symbols; and there are situations in which refusal to provide manuals in the required language could inhibit communication or affect the safe use of technical products. There is also the fear in some markets that failure to provide a translated manual will affect the product's image adversely. The demand for translated manuals can be expected to continue in the majority of international customer/supplier relationships for some time to come. How can the CFE development contribute to such a situation?

Since CFE has a limited vocabulary, and a 'one word – one meaning' principle, it represents an ideal form of translation input. The translator can rely on the definition of the word as shown in the dictionary provided. Furthermore, the short clear sentences are simple to translate and result in short clear sentences in the translated version. Thus the improvement in readability is maintained and the technical correctness ensured.

The requirement for the translator to be familiar with the company product range is largely removed. Translation is fast and accurate, the translator's skill being applied to matters such as the foreign syntactical requirements instead of sorting out complicated constructions and inconsistent nomenclature in the original English version. In certain applications, such as text specially written for data transmission or in specifications, the consistent meaning of a given word can eliminate editing entirely.

THE ILSAM LANGUAGE

Finally, it is necessary to explain the term ILSAM, which is the name used for the language in its most recent form when made available under licence to other companies and organizations outside the USA and Canada. The reference to its 'most recent form' indicates that field trials have shown the need for slight changes; these have been made and an amended vocabulary issued. The language has now been adopted by a number of leading companies and suitable nomenclature developed for their specific needs.

The application of constraints to technical writing has meant that the ILSAM texts are now suitable for computer processing. Current developments include computer programs for word analysis activities and for editing text to ensure compliance with the ILSAM vocabulary.

When translating it is a simple matter to produce tape libraries of the 800 words in ILSAM as both English and foreign versions. The translator can then use an electronic terminal to extract the words required for sentence construction, arranging them in the correct order before sending them to a print-out device or to a photocomposer or other printing equipment. Experiments in the USA indicate a large increase in translation speed and virtual elimination of translation errors using the method.

It is difficult to imagine that there can be a company which will not adopt this system and obtain great benefit from its use. As von Glasenapp commented: 'After three years of intense application of the system we are convinced that this is one step in the direction of future worldwide information distribution. The limitations were clear from the outset but the limits of its application cannot be visualized at this time'.

EXAMPLE

Maintenance	*Original text*	*Simplified version*

	AXLES
	CHANGING THE OIL
	  NOTE: Both front and rear axles are drained and filled in the same manner.
	1. Operate the machine until normal operating temperature is reached. Park the machine on level ground, completely lower the bucket, apply the parking brake and shut down the engine.
	2. Remove filler plug (1, Figure 7) and the drain plug (2).
	3. After the oil stops draining install the drain plug.
	4. Move the machine so the planetary drain plug is in the position shown in Figure 8.
	5. Shut down the engine and apply the parking brake.
	6. Remove the planetary drain (Figure 8).
	7. After the oil stops draining install the plug.
	8. Repeat steps 4 through 6 for the opposite planetary on the same axle.
	9. Fill the axle up to the bottom of the filler hole. Refer to 'LUBRICANT SPECIFICATIONS AND CAPACITIES CHART' in Section 7 for grade of lubricant specified.
	10. Install the filler plug.
	11. Operate the machine slowly for a short period of time in order for the oil to become distributed throughout the axle and planetaries.
	12. Stop the machine, completely lower the bucket, apply the parking brake and shut down the engine.
	13. Remove filler plug (1). If oil level is low add oil as necessary.
		THE FRONT AND REAR AXLES
		TO CHANGE THE OIL
		  NOTE: Use the same procedure to drain the oil from both the front and rear axles. Start the procedure with the front axle.
		TO DRAIN THE OIL
		1. Operate the machine until the engine temperature gauge indicates 100°F. Put the machine on flat ground. Lower the bucket fully. Stop the engine and engage the parking brake.
		2. Remove the filler plug (1) and the drain plug (2).
		3. After all the oil is drained, install the drain plug.
		4. Make sure the machine is in the position shown in Figure 8.
		5. Stop the engine and engage the parking brake.
		6. Remove the drain plug for the planetary gears.
		7. When you have drained all the oil, install the drain plug.
		8. To remove the oil from the opposite planetary gear, on the same axle, repeat steps 4, 5 and 6 above.
		TO FILL THE FRONT AND REAR AXLES WITH OIL:
		1. Get the correct grade and amount of lubricant from the 'Lubricant Specifications and Capacities Chart' on page 4, section 7.
		2. Fill the axle until you see the oil on the bottom of the hole for the filler plug.
		3. Install the filler plug.
		4. Operate the machine at a slow speed for 10 minutes.

Comments

In the ILSAM version, the instructions are precise, and are arranged in logical order. The expression 'Shut Down' is replaced by 'Stop'. The writer has included more facts; for example, the temperature is quoted as 100 degrees.

Steering Gear

Remove steering gear

1. Disconnect transmission control linkages (1) and (3).
2. Disconnect control linkage (5) for steering control valve.
3. Remove nut (2) and arm (4) from steering gear.
4. Remove bolts (6) that hold bracket for steering gear to dash.
5. Remove bolts that hold steering column to dash. Remove steering gear and column as a unit. Weight is 150 lb.

Install steering gear

1. Put steering gear and column (1) in position in machine.
2. Install bolts that hold steering column to dash.
3. Install bolts that hold bracket (3) to dash.
4. Connect transmission control linkages (2) and (6).
5. Connect control linkage (4) for steering valve.
6. Install arm and nut (5) on steering gear. Tighten nut to a torque of 450 ± 25 lb ft.

Comments

The repeated use of a limited number of verbs in the ILSAM vocabulary helps the reader and the translator.

Cargo Guides and Latches – description and operation

NOTE: This is part of a chapter from an aircraft manual which was sent for conversion to ILSAM. Conversion to ILSAM is difficult without access to the original data because usually more information is found to be necessary. In this example we were able to apply some basic rules of ILSAM but a number of questions remained unanswered.

1. General (Reference – Figure 001)

Containers or pallets in the cargo compartment are held in their correct positions by the cargo guides and latches. The forward compartment has latches for containers and pallets. The aft compartment has latches for containers only.

Some of the guides and latches have a single function and operate only as latches or as guides. Some have a double function and operate both as latches and guides.

All guides and latches are known as X, Y or Z guides and latches, according to the direction of the effect or effects when they are operated. The effects may be in

X direction (longitudinal)
Y direction (lateral)
Z direction (vertical)

Some have effect in more than one direction.

CHAPTER 7

Printing Simply Explained

by

JOHN WAKEFORD

Printing, in the true sense of the word as opposed to office duplicating methods, is a very old craft. It has developed over the years into a highly specialized industry which, today, employs skilled technicians and uses some of the most modern techniques and machinery available. Because of its specialized nature, this chapter does not attempt to give an authoritative exposition of printing procedures, techniques and equipment; there are many excellent books available on the subject – some dealing with single aspects of it such as typefaces or special machinery. Instead, the object of this chapter is to acquaint the reader very broadly with the three main printing methods, and to describe how material is processed by a printer. From the general information given, publications staff should be able to discuss their particular needs with a printer in commonly-understood terms.

THE THREE MAIN PRINTING METHODS

The three main printing methods used in professional printing establishments are: letterpress, intaglio and lithography (*see* Figure 7.1). There are variations on these methods, but the reproducing mechanics remain basically the same.

Letterpress   Letterpress uses the relief method in which the image to be reproduced stands out in exactly the same way as the characters on a rubber stamp or a typewriter. Ink is deposited on to the relief image and the image is then impressed on to the paper to leave a reverse of the image. Such direct impression means that the image to be reproduced must read the wrong way. (Wrong reading is the printing term used when the image reads the wrong way round, as seen in a mirror.) This is one disadvantage of the method; the accuracy of the composed text cannot really be ascertained until it is printed. To overcome this obstacle, an initial print (called a

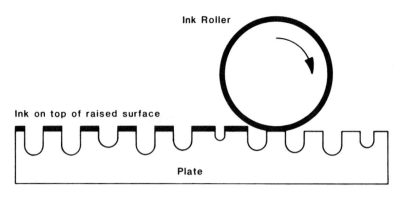

The Letterpress principle

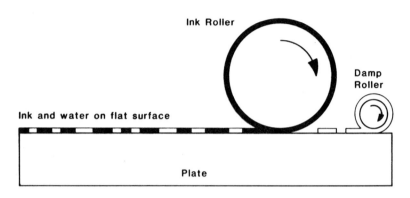

The Lithographic principle

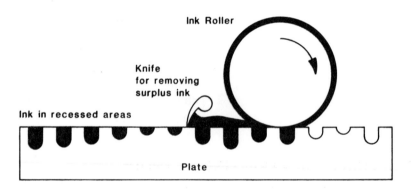

The Intaglio principle

Fig. 7.1   The principles of letterpress, lithographic and intaglio printing.

galley proof) is made on cheap paper. This is then used by the printer's customer to make proof corrections for the guidance of the printer.

A major advantage of the letterpress method is its robustness and consequent capability of producing many thousands of copies without deterioration in the quality of print.

Intaglio   Intaglio uses the recessed method in which the image to be reproduced is etched away.

A sophisticated process of engraving (referred to as photogravure) is involved to obtain this etched image, which consists of identical-size square pits varying in depth according to the density of 'tone' required.

The resultant plate bearing the etched image is covered with ink and then scraped with a knife so as to leave ink only in the etched pits. The image is then impressed on to the paper.

Because of the varying tone that can faithfully be reproduced, the intaglio method is usually used for high-quality colour printing. But because of the expense incurred in producing the engraved printing cylinders, the process can only be cost-effective if long runs are to be carried out. Consequently, the intaglio method is unlikely to be used for printing technical handbooks, which usually have relatively short runs.

Lithography Lithography uses the planographic method in which the image to be reproduced is neither in relief nor etched away. Instead, the image (which is processed on to a special plate) is prepared in such a way as to give it grease-receptive properties. Working on the principle that grease and water do not mix, water is applied to the plate to make the non-image area ink repellent so that, when greasy ink is applied to the whole area, only the greasy image will accept the ink. The ink is then transferred from the greasy image on to the paper. However, since the image to be reproduced reads the right way, the printed image will read the wrong way. For this reason the greasy image is first transferred to an intermediate rubber blanket on the print machine, and via this offset blanket to the paper. This process is referred to as offset lithography.

Offset lithography offers many advantages for the small-quantity reproduction of technical manuals, and is the method normally used by technical publications organizations. One advantage is that the matter to be reproduced can be read the right way throughout the text composition and platemaking stages. Because of this the material for printing, especially the text, is usually prepared and checked in the publications department itself, using standard office typewriters or word processors (*see* Chapter 9).

PROCESSING OF MATERIAL BY THE PRINTER

All material for printing comes under two categories: text (referred to as copy), and illustrations. Illustrations, in turn, fall into two categories: line illustrations, which are inked-line drawings usually drawn in black ink on a white background, and tone illustrations such as photographs, which have a variable contrast in their image density (the tone). The preparation of this material as artwork prior to being submitted to the printer is discussed in Chapters 4 and 8.

How the material is processed by the printer depends on the type of reproduction method to be used. The following is a general guide giving the procedures for processing material for offset lithography and for letterpress printing. (Intaglio is not dealt with for the reasons stated earlier.)

Processing for Offset When offset lithography is to be used, the printer is usually provided with
Lithography the text already quality-typed and set out on a page-for-page basis, including any in-text line illustrations. This is known as camera-ready copy, or material that is ready to be put in front of a process camera or into a platemaker. The process camera can produce either a film negative or a

projection diffusion transfer, each being a stage in the production of a lithographic printing plate. The platemaker can produce an electro-static or a contact diffusion transfer; these are discussed more fully under the section Lithographic Plates (*see* page 137).

If any of the in-text illustrations is a photograph or tone illustration, then the appropriate space will have been left on the camera-ready page and the illustration supplied separately with instructions as to any reduction and identification so that it will be inserted on the correct page.

The exception to providing camera-ready copy is when the text has been quality-typed on to a special paper known as direct image plates. These can be printed (machined) without any further print-image processing. The difference between a paper plate and an offset plate produced via the process camera is also discussed in more detail under the section Lithographic Plates.

Much emphasis has been placed on 'quality typing'. The quality of the initial image on the camera-ready copy (or direct image paper plate) is very important; the combined skills of the processing photographer, platemaker, and print machine minder cannot reproduce an image better than the initial image.

In addition to the package of camera-ready copy, the printer will also expect accompanying instructions and (preferably) a 'dummy' or page-for-page make-up of the complete job. From these instructions, the printer will plan the flow and distribution of the job through his establishment and organize the use of the print machines. This organization of the print machines is most important from the point of view of economy, especially when colour work is involved.

Photocomposition   Although in most technical publications work the camera-ready copy text which forms the printing image is produced directly from a good quality typewriter or word-processor printer, there are occasions when it is advantageous to have the printer use photographic methods to produce the text; high-quality sales promotion material and non-roman language text such as Arabic are two examples.

Early photosetting machines produce positive prints of the typeface required from negative typeface images stored on film. The optical system is adjustable so that a given type negative can be used to produce a wide range of sizes.

Later machines use a computer memory to store the type information. Each letter is formed from a large number of dots, each of which has its own binary co-ordinates (*see* Figure 7.2). The scanning light beam of the

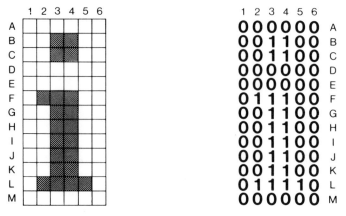

Fig. 7.2   *Simplified principle of digital photosetting.*

photo-reproduction system is switched on or off according to the commands of the computer. Variations in size and spacing are achieved by software commands.

The Process Camera To produce a negative, or a projection diffusion transfer, each camera-ready page is photographed by a process camera, which is no different in principle from a conventional hand-held camera. The base of the process camera rides on a rigid trackway so that the distance between its lens and the copyholder can be varied. The copyholder consists of a baseboard and a glass cover, and is sealed so that a vacuum can be applied within it to ensure that the copy is maintained perfectly flat while being photographed.

The size of the image is determined by the distance between the camera lens and the copyholder, and is set either by observing the image projected by the lens on to the grid of a ground-glass screen at the rear of the camera, or by referring to calibrations marked off along the camera track. (Fully automated cameras are available that only require the enlargement/reduction ratio to be typed in. The electronics in the camera work out the exposure and shutter speed for the shot required.)

Normally, camera-ready text pages are photographed at 1:1 ratio (size-for-size). For line illustrations and photographs which are to be reduced, the appropriate reduction instructions are included on the artwork. A standard reduction ratio of 2:1 or 3:2 is usually specified so as to give sharper definition, and to maintain an order which eliminates continuous repositioning and refocusing of the camera during batch work.

The photographic image obtained by the process camera from text and line diagrams is called a litho negative or a litho positive. In the former, the image is transparent and the surrounding area is opaque; in the latter, the image is opaque and the surrounding area is transparent. The choice of positive or negative depends on the type of lithographic plate to be made.

Half-tones A conventional photographic negative or positive image consists of gradated tones – from transparent to opaque. During the printing operation, a uniform film of ink is applied to the printing plate; the ink only 'understands' image, to which it adheres, or no image, from which it will be repelled. It cannot understand gradations of image. The illusion of gradations of tone is achieved by printing black dots of different sizes, but with a constant distance between centres (*see* Figure 7.3). The large dots create an illusion of dark grey and the small dots light grey. The transformation of tones to dots is achieved during the process camera stage by interposing a screen in front of the film.

Two types of screen may be used. One consists of two sheets of plate glass on each of which a series of parallel lines is etched and then filled in

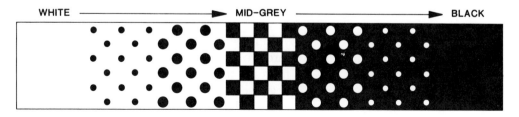

Tone gradations

Fig. 7.3   Half-tone principle showing gradations of tone.

with black pigment. The sheets are then sealed together so that the lines intersect each other at right angles to form an overall lattice pattern of square-shaped windows. The other type is a contact screen which is a sheet of film carrying a pattern of dots. Referred to as 'vignetted dots', they have solid cores which fade away towards their circumference. The overall effect is similar to that described for the plate glass screen.

Both glass and contact screens vary in their fineness depending on production requirements. The degree of fineness is dictated by the number of ruled lines to the inch, and varies from 55 to 175 lines to the inch for glass screens, and from 50 to 250 lines to the inch for contact screens. The most common screen rulings for offset lithography are 120 and 133 lines to the inch (although for fine-quality reproduction a 150 screen may be used). For monochrome work, the lines usually run at 45 degrees and the lines and apertures are of equal width.

If the half-tone being processed by the camera forms part of a page of text, then the half-tone negative is stripped into the appropriate space already left in the negative of the text. The negative is now complete with all its matter (a combination of line and tone) ready for platemaking.

Colour   If line diagrams are to be printed in more than one colour, then artwork will have been produced to meet this requirement. For example, if a pipework diagram in black is to have direction-of-flow arrows in red, two pieces of artwork are involved. One is the main diagram showing the pipework; the other diagram shows only the arrows, accurately positioned relative to a set of registration marks placed just outside the image area. When these registration marks are overlaid with corresponding registration marks on the main diagram, the arrows appear in the correct place by the pipework.

These registration marks are most important to the printer, and will appear on each litho negative or positive, and on the subsequent litho-plates.

If a colour line diagram forms part of a page of text, then the black component of the diagram is stripped into the appropriate space already left in the negative of the text. The negative is now complete as a page, ready for platemaking.

To reproduce a colour photograph (including colour transparencies) for colour printing, the original photographic image must be separated at the process camera stage into black and three primary colours: yellow, magenta (red) and cyan (blue). This is known as colour separation, and is achieved by making four, separate exposures, each via an appropriate colour filter. (The half-tone screen must also be used because the subject is a photograph consisting of various tones.)

A violet filter is used to produce a negative representing the yellow components of the image, a green filter for a magenta negative and an orange filter for a cyan negative; in each case, the colours are complementary. To produce the black negative, a pale yellow filter is necessary.

Enlarging on this principle of colour separation, consider an exposure through the violet filter (*see* Figure 7.4). This filter will allow all the light from the primary colours except yellow to pass from the original to the negative. All the negative except the 'yellow' areas is therefore exposed; conversely, the 'yellow' areas will show as transparent on the negative.

Before exposure for each colour separation, the camera operator alters the angle of the half-tone screen. This ensures that the half-tone dots representing the tone of any one primary colour are slightly offset from the

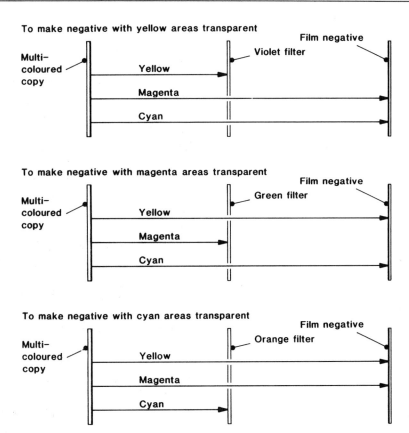

Fig. 7.4   Colour separation.

half-tone dots representing the tones of the other two primary colours and the black tone. The reason for this juxtaposition of the dots is as follows. When the page bearing the printed yellow image is printed, the ink must be allowed to dry before it is passed through the printing machine again to have the cyan image printed. The colour green is obtained by the merging of primary colours yellow and cyan. But in printing the inks do not physically merge; each colour is allowed to dry separately. Instead, the optical illusion of green is achieved by having the cyan dots printed in close juxtaposition to the yellow dots; although in practice there is always some slight degree of super-imposition of the dots. The degree of angular displacement of the screen for each colour is critical, and undesirable 'moire' patterns can appear if the screen angles are incorrect. So much depends on the skill of the machine minder to print each of the four plates in perfect register one with the other. When magnified, the printed colour picture will reveal the dots in clusters, each constituting a rosette pattern.

If a colour half-tone forms part of a page of text, then the half-tone negative representing the black image areas is stripped into the appropriate space already left in the negative of the text. The negative is now complete with all its black matter (a combination of line and tone), ready for platemaking.

Lithographic plates   A lithographic plate has an image area which is grease receptive so that it attracts the greasy printing ink, and a non-image, water receptive, area which is dampened during the printing process so that it repels the greasy ink.

There are four basic types of lithographic plate: the direct-typing paper plate, the electro-statically produced paper plate, the diffusion transfer plate and the photochemically produced metal plate.

The direct-typing paper plate has a limited use for short runs. A special greasy ribbon is fitted to the typewriter, and this imprints a greasy image on the specially coated paper.

The electro-statically produced paper plates are also used for short runs. These plates can be made very quickly by feeding the camera copy directly into the platemaking machine.

The diffusion transfer plate can be either a metal or a paper plate. Metal plates are made of aluminium and are often known as 'foil' plates; they are suitable for up to 10,000 copies or, when lacquered, will produce up to 25,000 copies. Paper diffusion transfer plates are suitable for up to 3,000 copies. The diffusion transfer plate is made from a diffusion transfer negative which can only be used once. Two types of negative material are available: 'contact' – for exposure direct from the original using a vacuum exposing unit, or 'projection' – for exposure using a plate camera. The projection method requires a dark room for the plate camera, the contact method requires subdued light only. Once the negative has been exposed it is brought into contact with the plate through a small roller processing unit. A variety of 'receiver' papers is also available for producing copy prints by the same method.

The diffusion transfer method offers both platemaking and artwork production at relatively low cost. Print quality is generally accepted to be only slightly inferior to that of pre-sensitized metal plates.

Metal plates, which are used for longer runs and high quality work, are produced by photographing the camera copy so that the printing image is transferred to a film, and then using this film to produce the image and non-image areas by photo-chemical processes.

There are various types of metal plate with different characteristics, and the technology of platemaking is very complex. However, this is not the concern of technical publications personnel, and is therefore outside the scope of this book. The important thing is to make your requirements quite clear to the printer so that he can choose an appropriate plate. If, for example, there is a possibility of a future reprint, the printer should be informed of this.

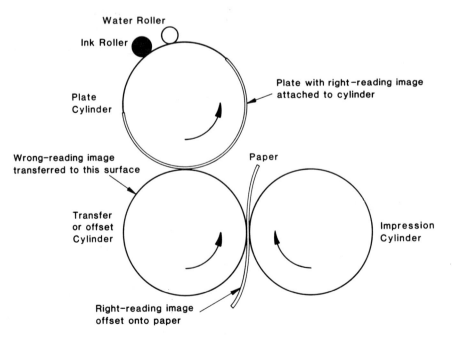

Fig. 7.5   Principle of offset-lithography press.

The Lithographic Printing Operation In the printing operation, the lithographic plate is attached to a rotating cylinder. As it rotates, the plate is first dampened by dampening rollers, then inked by inking rollers.

For offset lithography, the image on the plate must be right-reading. Initially, the image is transferred from the right-reading plate, which is fitted to the plate cylinder on the offset machine, on to a rubber blanket on the transfer cylinder. The image, now wrong-reading, is then offset by pressure from the impression cylinder on to paper to become right-reading again (*see* Figure 7.5). Although this process may seem to be roundabout, it has advantages which have already been discussed. In addition, by using a rubber blanket to transfer the image from plate to paper, it is possible to print on the roughest papers as well as hard surfaces such as tin.

Processing for Letterpress   When letterpress is to be used, the printer is provided with clearly typed, double-spaced copy, artwork for all the various types of illustrations and full instructions as to the type of format and setting to be used. Although the format and setting will usually have been discussed with the printer, the following details must be clearly stated:

- Page size.
- Text measure (width), and number of columns. (Also define all margins.)
- Whether the text is to be justified or not.
- Typeface style (fount).
- Point size and body of the typeface.

With the exception of the last two, these instructions are obvious. Fount and typesize are briefly discussed at the end of this chapter; however, if their relevance is to be fully appreciated in the context of letterpress text composition, the reader should consult one of the many books available on the subject. In any case, always rely upon the printer's experience and advice in this and other areas of letterpress printing.

Letterpress text   Letterpress type is wrong-reading, so that a direct print from it reads the right way round.

In the early days of printing, the individually cast letters were assembled ('set') by hand in a tray known as a composing stick. Many of the printing terms used today originate from these early processes. The small letters a to z became known as 'lower case' because they were always kept in the lower storage case. Hand setting is still occasionally used for business cards and similar small jobs.

Nowadays most letterpress typesetting is done by machines, which cast the type as required. There are two basic types of mechanical typesetting machine: *Linotype* which casts a complete line at a time, and *Monotype* which casts each letter individually. In each case, the machine is controlled from a keyboard.

When all the type has been 'composed', it is placed in a larger tray called a galley which contains all the other type to be printed. At this stage a 'galley-proof' can be printed to enable a proof-reader to check for any errors or faults in the quality of the type. After this proofing stage, the long strips of type are split into page lengths and a further proof is taken and checked.

The pages of text are then positioned in a steel frame (chase) and locked firmly into position. This complete assembly is known as the printing forme. After a last proof has been taken and finally checked, it can be put on to a letterpress machine for printing.

Letterpress illustrations   If any illustrations – whether line or tone – are included in the page formats, all the appropriate artwork will go in front of the process camera for the purpose of reduction, and to obtain the negative required for subsequent photoengraving. If there are tone illustrations, these will have to be photographed through a screen, as described for lithography.

For photoengraving (in which the image on the printing plate is in relief) the image on the negative must be wrong-reading. This right-reading is achieved during the process-camera stage by using a lens prism, or by straight line image reversal.

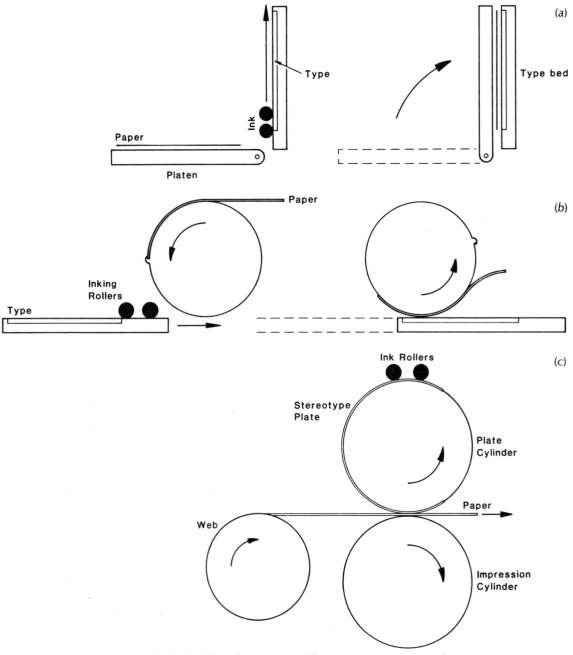

Fig. 7.6   Three basic types of letterpress printing machines.
(a) Platen machine. (b) Cylinder machine. (c) Rotary machine.

The negative produced by the process camera is held securely against the printing plate in a vacuum frame, and then exposed to light. The metal printing plate is coated with a light sensitive compound, which is hardened when exposed to light. When the plate is exposed to light through the negative, the plate areas corresponding to the transparent areas of the negative are hardened by the light. The unhardened areas of the compound are soluble in water and washed off. The hardened areas are then further hardened by the application of heat. Acid etching is then carried out on the unhardened areas, which leaves the printing image standing proud.

The letterpress printing operation There are three basic types of letterpress machine, which are illustrated in Figure 7.6.

On the *platen* machine the type, which often is hand set, is fixed to a perpendicular type bed. The paper is placed on a *platen*, while the inked rollers run over the type. Then the platen swings upwards to press the paper against the inked type. Platen machines are usually used for small printing jobs.

On the *cylinder* machine the type is placed on a horizontal surface. Initially the type plate moves across (to the left on Figure 7.6) to pass under the inked rollers. Then the type plate moves back to the right, and at the same time the cylinder carrying the paper revolves to bring the paper into contact with the inked type.

For the *rotary* machines, the type as originally set is not placed on the machine but is used to mould a curved *stereotype* plate. The stereotype plate is then attached to the rotating cylinder of the press. Paper stored on a reel (web) is fed between the impression and plate cylinders. The larger rotary presses have a second set of cylinders so that both sides of the paper are printed at the same time. Multi-colour printing machines have additional sets of ink and plate rollers, one set for each colour, so that each of the colours can be printed as the paper runs through the machine. Newspapers are usually printed on large rotary presses.

TYPE MEASUREMENT AND SOME COMMON PRINTING TERMS

Figure 7.7 shows a letterpress type letter and illustrates some of the terms used in typography. These terms may still be used, even when printing other than by letterpress. In particular, point size is still used to denote a size of type. (*Note:* The continental point size differs slightly from the British.) As can be seen from the illustration, point size is determined by the size of the body, not by the size of the letter. It is therefore possible to have type of the same point size with letters of different sizes (*see* Figure 7.8).

The following is a list of some of the printing terms that may be useful for personnel engaged in technical publications:

Bleed
When a block or border of colour has to be printed right up to the edge of the paper, the image is produced so that it slightly overlaps the size of the final printed paper. It is then printed on oversize paper and trimmed down to the final size required. The amount it is printed oversize is called the bleed.

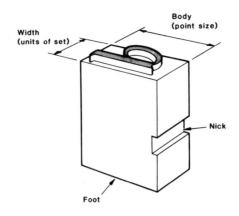

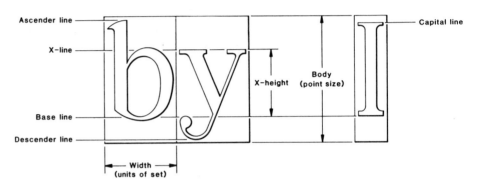

Fig. 7.7   Basic type dimensions.

Body
A letterpress term relating to the dimensions of the metal on which the letter is set (*see* Figure 7.7).

Bold
A heavier, blacker typeface, used mainly for headings and for emphasis in text.

This line is printed in bold type.

Dummy
A replica of the book or document for the guidance of the printer, showing the disposition of all the pages, illustrations, etc. Nowadays it is common to use photocopies of the camera copy for compiling the dummy.

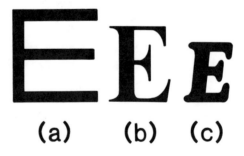

(a) 72pt Microgramma Medium Extended
(b) 72pt Times Bold·
(c) 72pt Knightsbridge

Fig. 7.8   Three letters, each 72 point nominal point size.

Em
A printing measurement based on either the square of the body, or the width of the widest character in a fount (usually M) (*see also* Pica).

Fount
A complete set of type of one particular face and size. For example, 10 point Times Roman.

Galley proof
The first proof in letterpress printing, taken when the type is set in long trays (galleys), before it is divided into pages. Illustration proofs are supplied separately from the text (*see also* page proofs).

Imposition
The arrangement of the type for a number of pages, so that these pages can be printed at once. For example, with a sixteen page imposition eight pages are printed on one side of a sheet of paper and eight on the other. The arrangement is such that, when folded, the pages will be in the right order, ready for cutting and trimming.

Italics
A sloping type which originated in Italy and is now frequently used for emphasis.

This line is printed in italics.

Justified text
Arrangement of the type so that both ends of the lines are vertically aligned.

Laser printer
A type of non-impact printer (*see* page 179).

Leading
A term from letterpress printing to denote additional spacing between lines of type (achieved by adding strips of lead). The term is nevertheless used for printing carried out other than by letterpress.

Lower case
This term denotes letters which are not capitals. It derives from the early days of hand-set letterpress when the lower case letters were kept in the lower case of type, whereas the capitals (upper case letters) were kept in the upper case of type.

Manuscript
This term, often abbreviated to MS, now applies to both hand written and typed copy.

Non-impact printer
A development of the photocopier (*see* page 179).

Page proof
The proof of the complete page, including illustrations, ready for printing.

Pagination
The term used for the numbering of pages.

Pica
Pica, short for 'Pica Em', is an archaic measurement derived from the width of a 12 point letter M. One 'pica' equals ⅙ in. Nowadays it usually is more practical to make measurements in millimetres. However, tables for 'casting off', that is working out the number of characters per line, still use 'picas' as a unit of measurement for the line width and depth of text.

Point

The term used to denote the size of type. It originated in letterpress printing and derives from the size of the body on which the type is set (*see* Figure 7.7). Dimensionally, one point equals ⅟₇₂ in.; the European point (Didot) is slightly larger (by 0.025 mm). However, it is important to understand that because 'point' derives from the size of the type body, not the size of the character, the height of a letter cannot be determined directly from the point size. Thus 12 point letters are not all $12 \times \frac{1}{72} = \frac{1}{6}$ in. high. As shown in Figure 7.8, there can be considerable differences in the size of letters, each having the same nominal point size. Sometimes in letterpress printing, to achieve extra space between lines, letters of a particular type size were cast on bodies normally used for a larger type size; for example 10 point type cast on a 12 point body. Even when letterpress printing is not used, the term 'ten on twelve' may still be used to denote 10 point type with extra spacing between the lines.

These two lines are set 10 on 10 xxxxxxxxxxxxxxxxxxxxxxxxxxxxxxxxxxxxxxxxxxxxxx
xxxxxxxxxxxxxxxxxxxxxxxxxxxxxxxxxxxxxxxxxxxxxxxxxxxxxxxxxxxxxxxxxxxxxxxxxxxx
These two lines are set 10 on 12 xxxxxxxxxxxxxxxxxxxxxxxxxxxxxxxxxxxxxxxxxxxxxx
xxxxxxxxxxxxxxxxxxxxxxxxxxxxxxxxxxxxxxxxxxxxxxxxxxxxxxxxxxxxxxxxxxxxxxxxxxxxx

Range left/right

Range left means vertically align the left-hand ends of the lines of type; range right align the right-hand ends.

Recto

A right-hand page (*see also* verso). By convention, right-hand pages are always odd-numbered. At times it may seem inconvenient to follow this convention, but experience teaches that deviation from the convention can often lead to misunderstanding and error.

Rule

A line, originally achieved by inserting metal strips ('rules').

Saddle stitched

The term used when pages are folded in two, then stapled or stitched along the central fold.

Serif/sans serif

Serif type has short cross lines at the end of each stroke of a letter; sans serif type does not.

This line is printed in serif type.
This line is printed in sans serif type.

Side Stitched

The term used when pages are stapled or stitched through the left-hand margin.

Upper Case

The printing term sometimes used for capitals (*see* lower case). However, 'caps' is a more common term.

Verso

The term for left-hand pages, which by convention are always even-numbered (*see* recto).

PAPER AND BINDING

The kind of paper and sort of binding will already have been discussed with the printer, since both items are factors in the costing of the printing job. Both items should suit the purpose of the document as well as the environment in which it will be used. For example, if the publication is a workshop manual, then one of the proprietary papers which can be moistened and wiped clean of oily finger marks could be specified.

There are several types of binding, but the one most frequently used for technical publications is the ring-type, which allows each page of the publication to be loose-leaf and therefore convenient for replacement when amendments to the handbook are issued.

CHAPTER 8

Preparing Material for Printing, and Quality Assurance Procedures

by
E. J. MARDEN

Although there are variations in the way a draft can be processed so that it finally appears as a finished publication, the detail and checks inherent in the conventional procedure have still to be covered, even though the steps may be taken out of sequence or in a modified form.

The procedures given in this chapter are comprehensive, and are designed to meet the needs of an organization publishing an extensive range of documents. Although all of these procedures will not apply to every organization, especially the smaller ones, the relevant procedures can easily be adapted to suit particular needs. The procedures given constitute a practical model on which publications quality assurance procedures can be based.

Normally, the sequence for producing a publication is: (a) commission, (b) draft, (c) type, (d) distribute for comment, (e) revise, (f) edit, (g) re-type, (h) continue cycle of (b) to (g) until final text is agreed, (j) prepare a manuscript for the printer's copy, for typesetting and first proof, (k) correct first proof and continue with further proofs until, (l) a final or page proof is available, (m) print off (press) as in the final or page proof, (n) bind and (o) distribute. Usually, drafting and working-up to the copy is done by one organization, typesetting and printing by another, with possibly a third doing the binding.

Nowadays, all these operations may well be performed within one organization, or they might be further fragmented. As it is not possible to cover all the permutations of equipment, personnel and resources, the conventional sequence will be described here, with digression only where this may be helpful. The particular circumstances for each job should guide the reader in making his own variations.

Accordingly, expressions such as 'printer', 'printer's copy', 'proof', etc., must be taken to refer to whoever or whatever they apply to in the particular circumstances.

Ideally, the layout, typesetting, printing process and type of binding should be decided before the first draft is typed (if possible, the layout should be decided before the first draft is written). To arrive at these decisions, it may be necessary to take into account a specification laid down by the 'customer', in which all such matters may be decided. Where the 'customer' is one's own employer, house rules and precedents may well provide sufficient guidance. In the absence of a specification or house rules, the following should be considered:

- Number of copies, number and size of pages.
- Budget for the job.
- Purpose of the finished article, and level of intelligence and expertise of expected users.
- Prestige sought and impact desired.
- Quality of paper.
- Typesetting, when related to in-house resources.
- Layout, when related to in-house resources, especially page layouts and justification of margins.
- Types of illustration and method of presentation, whether incorporated in text or separate from text, size (for example, throw-out, those which remain visible while other pages are read), line, tone, colour.
- Type of binding based on considerations of uniformity, durability, expected life, amendability.
- Availability of in-house equipment, materials, skills and labour.
- Cash outflow, where outside sources are to be engaged.

It is unlikely that the exact preparation procedure will be specified, and a knowledge of different methods can often save much money and time, dependent upon the equipment and facilities available to the personnel concerned with preparation.

This chapter examines the various printing processes which may be used; some factors affecting the choice of a suitable printing process; the processing of text; the processing of illustrations; and variations necessitated by the different printing processes. Information is also provided on records and special measures for interrelated documentation.

CHOICE OF PRINTING PROCESS

There may be no choice if the customer's specification states the process, but if one is not specified, then the standard of print production should be decided in consultation with the customer before a decision is taken. Once decided upon and depending upon equipment and facilities available, the method of preparing text and illustrations can be determined.

The main processes are discussed under their appropriate headings in the following paragraphs.

Offset Lithography This is the most usual method of printing technical publications. Quality of reproduction is good for both text and illustrations, and the machines normally print faster than in any other short-run printing method. A certain amount of operator skill is required to run the machines effectively, and setting-up time is a factor to be considered for very short runs of under 50 copies.

Offset-litho machines (the principles of operation of which are discussed in Chapter 7) are available with automatic control, which makes them effective for short runs and a large number of pages, for example, 100 copies of 250 pages. Bigger and more expensive machines are able to print more than one page at a time, and to cope with large illustrations. Generally, the larger machines are more expensive to use.

As a requisite for lithography is a lithographic plate suitable for the quantities to be run, any considerations must take account of the in-house equipment which can be used in preparing such a plate. Where acceptable typesetting can be achieved using in-house equipment, for example, office typewriter, 'golf-ball' machine with variable letter and line spacing, or word processor; there are three possible methods:

(a) Where the run is short, and there are no line illustrations which cannot be drawn directly on to the plate, it is possible for the text to be set directly on to a pre-sensitized paper plate, using an office typewriter or golf-ball machine fitted with a special ribbon. Such a process has drawbacks. Tone illustrations cannot be incorporated, and the wear characteristics of such plates are such that the plates do not store well once the initial run is complete.

(b) Where an electro-static platemaking machine is available, the text can be set on plain paper as camera copy, with tone and line illustrations being let in after the text has been produced. A paper plate produced by this method is good for between 700 to 1,000 copies, and will often run to 2,000.

(c) The text set as in (b) could be used to prepare a plate by photo-litho methods (*see* Chapter 7).

Where an acceptable text setting cannot be achieved using in-house equipment, typesetting will have to be done by an outside printer, and the nearest stage to this is printer's copy.

Whatever printing process is used, it is as well to remember that the quality of the finished work depends very much on the quality of the camera copy. Good quality results are never obtained from poor originals.

Letterpress   Letterpress is still a high-class alternative to offset lithography; the process is described in Chapter 7. Its quality and economy depend on the standards of workmanship and quality control within the printing house. Experience and personal contacts are the best guides as to where to place the work. The requisites for letterpress are printer's copy and either camera copy, or photoengraved blocks for the illustrative material.

Photocopying   For some jobs, photocopying, using modern equipment, good camera-ready copy and a properly set up machine, can be quite acceptable. However, as some machines have a metered charging system, it will be found that above a certain number of copies, it would be cheaper to use another method. Even on the latest machines photographs may not print too well, and even half-tone pictures may lose definition when reproduced by this means.

Wax Stencils   If none of the foregoing equipment is available, acceptable results may be obtained from cut wax stencils. With the early type of wax stencil machine, the typist's touch, or setting of any variable impression control on the typewriter (so as not to cut out completely the enclosed outlines, such as 'o' and 'e') and the setting up and inking of the duplicating machine, are important ingredients for success. Any illustrations, graphs, etc., obviously have to be very simple, and limited to line drawings with no fine detail and without too many deviations from straight lines.

Later wax stencil machines, with an electronic scanner and an electric spark device for cutting the stencil, are much more versatile. Further details of this type of machine are given in Chapter 9.

Conclusions The decision on whether the typesetting, printing and binding should be placed with an outside printer or be done in-house, will depend on the standards required for the job (as enumerated in the introduction to this chapter), the capabilities of the in-house staff and equipment and/or the willingness of outsiders to take on anything but the complete job.

PLANNING, TIMETABLE, CO-ORDINATION

For other than the simplest tasks, a timetable and a means of checking that it is being kept to are essential. Not only will it enable bookings to be made with the typing, illustrating, typesetting, printing, binding and distribution agencies, it should also help to eliminate the risk of essential personnel being absent at critical times. As with all timetables, the dates should work backwards from the completion date. Over-optimism on estimating the work rate should be avoided. It is wise not only to feed in a 'fumble factor' here and there, to guard against the unexpected, but also to bear in mind that the more people involved the greater will be the chance of delays. A specimen timetable is shown in the appendix to this chapter.

To guard against unwanted fragmentation of the job, suitably annotated job bags or working folders should be prepared, and should be used at all times except when papers are being worked on (*see also* the section on Records).

Where possible, a co-ordinator, empowered to make or endorse all decisions, should be nominated. All queries should be channelled through the co-ordinator, to avoid duplication of effort and conflict of ideas.

TEXT PREPARATION

Having established the end result of each stage of the text preparation, for example, potential camera copy from first draft onwards, typist's manuscripts, typescripts, draft copy and printer's copy, all activities should, ideally, be directed to achieving this end result by the most economical means.

It is assumed that drafting, typing and editorial staff are available, with access to a photocopying machine. With the advent of photocopiers and photolithography, the amount of re-typing from draft to draft can be reduced by 'cutting and sticking', whereby any text which is unaltered is cut out of the top copy of the preceding draft and stuck, in its sequence, into the succeeding draft. Small corrections made with a white correcting paint or correction tapes, can also help to avoid extensive re-typing. With care, single lines can be removed and replaced. It is advisable to retain all discarded material until the revised draft has been checked (*see also* the section on Records). Cutting and sticking is ideal for photolithography, as copy, the negative and sometimes the plate, can be retouched to eliminate join lines, etc.

Layout and Typography   Unless it is provided in the customer's specification, a layout or 'dummy' covering all foreseeable typographic conventions and layout features, should be prepared. This, plus the house rules for text preparation, should obviate the need for extensive re-typing or marking-up for the typesetter during the later stages.

The following layout and typography details may need to be decided.

(a) The image area and its position on the page in terms of the measurement of the type (*see* Chapter 7 for type measurement).

(b) The typographic conventions need to be settled, for example:

  (i) The point sizes and founts for the text, chapter numbers and titles, paragraph numbers and titles, etc. Where camera copy is not being prepared in-house, and printer's copy is the end result, it may be possible to agree conventions with the printer, which will obviate the need for repetitive marking of copy; for instance, the following conventions have been used by the author for many years, and could clearly be modified, or added to, to suit individual requirements.

- All chapter numbers and titles to be typed in capitals and underlined, and this to indicate 12 point Gill Bold.
- All main paragraph numbers and headings to be typed in capitals and not underlined, and this is to indicate 10 point Gill Medium.
- All subsidiary paragraph numbers and headings to be typed in capitals and lower case and underlined, and this to indicate 10 point Times New Roman Bold.

Where italic is required in the setting, the marginal notation 'ital' should complement a coloured underline to distinguish it from the underlining in the convention.

  (ii) Variation in point size for notes and footnotes, thus, if the text is to be 10 point, notes and footnotes could be 8 point.

  (iii) The titling and style for figures and tables, for example, all capitals, or capitals and lower case; position of title relative to figure or table (range-left, centred, above, below); fount(s) for titles and contents.

  (iv) The layout of tables, for example, column headings and columns (ranged-left, centred): alignment of columns, especially numbers, all decimal points aligned; all units, tens, hundreds, etc., aligned: location in relation to associated text (*see British Standards*, Chapter 10 for advice on presentation).

  (v) The layout (landscape or portrait) of figures; location in relation to text.

  (vi) Any paragraph numbering system, specifying sequence of numbers (one digit, two digits, three digits, (a), (b), etc., (i), (ii), etc., (1), (2), etc.). Indentations associated therewith in terms of typewriter spaces or ems.

Where camera copy is the aim from the start, lay sheets, with guide lines printed in feint blue ink (which does not photograph) are very useful. Lay sheets can be marked to indicate positions for such features as running heads, shoulder headings (*see* page 161), image area, indents, columns, page (folio) numbers. So that the typist can avoid unacceptable splitting of text at the end of a page, the lay sheet can also be marked to indicate how much space – within the image area, for example, 2 in., 1½ in., 1 in. – remains on the sheet. An alternative which can be effective and save time, is to include, outside the image area (also in non-photographic light blue) typewriter scales horizontally (i.e. 10 and 12 per inch) and a ⅙ in. scale, at least, down one side. As the margins change sides according to whether the page is right or left-handed, it may be advisable to prepare separate lay sheets, to obviate the need for the platemaker or printing machine operator to make the necessary adjustments.

Although typographic design is a separate subject, a few hints are apposite at this point.

(a) Except where the contrary is known to be the custom (as in some European countries) use a serif type where long passages are to be read, and restrict sans serif type to headings and display pieces.

(b) Keep the number of different typefaces to the minimum.

(c) Stay within a family of typefaces, where possible, and only go outside where a desired face is not available within the family.

(d) Be wary of the latest fashion.

(e) Where it is necessary to determine the amount of space which will be occupied by copy when set, the total number of characters and spaces in the typewritten copy should first be calculated by multiplying the number in an average line by the number of lines in the copy. A cast-off sheet, of the appropriate fount, will show how many characters, including spaces, can be set to the inch; this figure when taken in conjunction with the point size (for example 12 point has six lines to the inch), spacing between paragraphs and image area of the page, will enable a reasonable approximation to be made. A word count is not a reliable method of calculation.

Records Before beginning to type the drafts, a decision should be made as to the records required for each of the various stages.

It is advisable that any document, whether or not one of a series, be given an individual reference number, and that details of at least its title be entered in a register. In addition to the reference number, each draft which differs from its predecessor in any way, however slight, should be given a new draft number and date, which, in conjunction with the entries in the register, can then be used to establish the latest version. It can be most annoying to unwittingly work through an out-of-date draft.

A decision should also be made whether changes made from draft to draft need to be recorded. This can be simply done by using the typist's manuscripts as a record of each successive draft. The typist's manuscript should show the alterations in manuscript in the style for correcting printer's proofs, or in the form of deletions and 'Take in A, B, etc.' as well as the new draft number and date. Where a record is required of the source of each amendment, the amendments could be made on the manuscript in different coloured inks which are linked with the appropriate names on the first page of the document, or initials could be ringed and entered in the margin against each change.

Where documents are interrelated and subject to amendment, further records may be necessary. Details are given in the appendix to this chapter.

Preparation of Drafts While drafting, typing and processing the various drafts, it may be found desirable to use a series of progressive check lists, which will eventually lead to the desired end result with a minimum of effort. Suggested items for inclusion in a check list to be applied at this stage are given in the appendix to this chapter (*see* Check List for Preparation of Early Drafts).

The typist should be left in no doubt as to what is required. Where any doubt could arise, an instruction, ringed and prefixed 'TO TYPIST' (to distinguish it from copy) should be written in the margin. Where illustrations, tables, mathematical expressions, etc., are to be let into the text after it is typed, the position and amount of space to be left blank relative to the associated text, should be indicated.

Drafts should be typed on one side of the paper only, and should follow the layout dummy so far as is possible within the typographic limitations of the typewriter. They may, of course, be backed-up when copied and distributed. It is advisable, at the early draft stage, to use double-line spacing as this enables comments to be written between the lines. Where printer's copy is the end result, this double spacing will contribute to producing an acceptable manuscript, but with in-house camera copy in mind it may necessitate retyping in single-line spacing later on. The pros and cons of convenience versus extra typing should be considered, and in this respect a word processor scores, as it can print out in whichever line spacing is selected (*see* Chapter 9).

The top copy of each typed draft should be put aside in a protective cover. All editing work and the preparation of the typist's manuscript for the next stage should be done on suitably annotated copies, for example, 'Text Checker's Copy', 'Master Working Copy'. As the typist's manuscript will constitute the record, the top copy may, with luck, reduce the amount of retyping from one draft to the next by being cut and stuck in the preparation of the next draft; minor amendments being made on it using a white correcting paint or correction tapes. The top copy should remain unmarked so that extra copies may be taken, if needed.

Where this procedure is adopted, the typist's manuscript, which will be a consolidation of all the comments and corrections from the working copies, should take the form of a complete copy of the previous draft, with all changes being shown in the style for correcting printer's proofs. Where large parts of the text are to be replaced, the manuscript should show the deletion, with the new material identified separately, and introduced by a note to the typist such as – 'Take in A (three sheets)'.

Taking account of the effort put in by author, commentators and editor, the checking of typed drafts should always be treated seriously. Each draft should be checked using the proof-reading procedure described later in this chapter, and ideally, author, editor and typist should take no part in text checking. However, if participation is unavoidable, the author or editor may read from the copy, but not the typist, who may repeat errors of interpretation. The normal rule of proof-reading, that reading aloud should only be done from the copy, will have to be modified to suit the circumstances.

Where the proof-reading procedure is not possible, the revised draft should be checked against the typist's manuscript, preferably by someone not connected with preparing the manuscript, and certainly not by the typist.

Vetting and Editing Once he has prepared his draft, it is normal practice for the author to send it to selected persons for comment. Usually comments are restricted to technical matters. Unless a commentator has agreed otherwise, it is sensible to allow adequate time for comments to be made. A good general rule is to relate the time for comment to the number of pages in the document, for example, in accordance with the formula:

$$N = 2 + \sqrt[3]{n}$$

Where N = weeks

n = pages.

The formula gives a minimum of three weeks for a one-page document, and thus allows for the commentator to be absent for a fortnight at the time of receipt.

Following the receipt of all comments, the author will produce a further draft, which will then be submitted for editing (*see* Chapter 5). The typist's manuscript for this further draft should be produced in accordance with the procedure in the preceding paragraphs, either by the author himself, or otherwise, as agreed by him.

After editing, the preparation of the typist's manuscript for the next stage should be agreed in consultation with the editor. As he will be working from notes of his discussions with the author, the editor will probably prefer to prepare the manuscript himself.

Final Draft The procedure for deciding that a draft is 'final' should be established. Normally, it is determined by agreement of the co-ordinator or other responsible personnel with the author and editor, but sometimes, as with papers for learned societies, a referee has the final word. Before presenting the draft for agreement, any check lists used in its preparation should be examined to confirm that everything has been completed satisfactorily, and has been signed off. Where revisions have been made, it should be verified that the dates on which the checks were done are compatible with the dates when the revisions were incorporated.

PREPARATION OF PRINTER'S COPY

Unless the drafting and equipment used has resulted in text and artwork which is suitable for assembling the camera copy for platemaking, the final draft has to be processed to convert it into printer's copy, such as will enable the printer to provide a first (or galley) proof. Even where there is no need for typesetting and proofing, some parts of this section may be appropriate (for example, page numbering, space for in-text tables).

A final draft, arrived at by following the procedures set out in this chapter, should go far towards providing acceptable printer's copy. Where a layout (or dummy) has been produced, it should be called up for the printer's copy. Where the layout had been submitted to the printer for agreement, such agreement should be re-affirmed.

In addition to those matters covered by the layout, which normally form 'standing instructions' covering typography and general layout only, other details which arise from page to page need to be covered by separate directions. Do not have standing instructions for items which occur only rarely in the text; it is safer to write a separate command each time, especially with lengthy documents which may take days to set, and be handled on different shifts by different compositors.

All steps should be taken to eliminate the possibility of anything being set, other than in the required way. Suggested items for inclusion in a check list to be applied at this stage are given in the appendix to this chapter. However, there are some matters which justify a few extra words.

Notes to Printer   Any instructions to the printer and written on the copy must be clearly distinguished from text by writing the words 'TO PRINTER' at the start of the instruction and ringing the whole, otherwise the words may be read as part of the text, and be set.

Ambiguities   The text should be scrutinized for any parts where the setting is open to doubt, and a note should be written in the margin to clarify what is required. Such notes will help to avoid costly corrections. Remember that corrections may involve hand work, and can cost 25 times as much as an initial correct setting.

Page Numbering   Each page of the copy must be numbered consecutively in the top right-hand corner, with the total number of pages for each batch indicated on the first page. Where a batch is not the complete job this should be clearly stated, as should the relative position of any copy to follow, whether preceding or succeeding. If it is desired to identify each page of copy with its chapter or section this may be done by including the chapter or section number as part of the numbering system in the top right-hand corner. Thus, Chapter 1 pages would be numbered 1.2, 1.3, 1.4, etc.

Once the numbering has been applied, pages may be deleted or added without renumbering throughout. A page which is deleted would remain numbered in the copy but its text would be deleted. Additional pages would be numbered in sequence with a suffix, thus '20a', '20b'. Where this is done it would be advisable to indicate on page 20 that pages 20a and 20b follow; this guards against a page becoming detached from the copy and not being noticed, as there would be no obvious break in the sequence of page numbering. The total on the first page should be amended and qualified accordingly.

Gaps in Copy   Any unintentional gaps in the copy should be closed up, either by cutting and sticking, or where this is not desired, by adding an instruction to the printer identifying the text to be run on to close the gap.

Space for In-text Illustrations and Tables   Whatever decisions are made on the position and format of illustrations and tables (*see* the section 'Layout and Typography') it is necessary to indicate where space should be allowed to accommodate them (they are normally let in at the second or page proof stage).

Where illustrations and tables are to be integrated into the text the dimensions and positions of vertical and horizontal space to be left should be indicated. As the paging of the printer's copy is unlikely to be identical to that of the set pages, the location of the reserved space is best indicated by asking for it to be left 'as close as possible to this paragraph' or 'as close as possible before or after this paragraph, or sentence', and so on.

Where illustrations and tables are to be grouped together, appropriate instructions about the reservation of pages should be given.

Where a title does not form part of an illustration or table to be inserted later, the reference and title should be included as part of the copy; thus 'Fig. 1 A TYPICAL TEST RIG', and the printer should be asked to set this in the desired position relative to the space.

Mathematics and Signs and Symbols

Where the mathematics to be set are at all complicated (that is going beyond arabic numerals) careful thought must be given not only to preparing the printer's copy, but also to the preparation of the camera copy or photoengraved block. Even though some type families have their mathematical characters, and special mathematical setting systems are available on filmsetters and letterpress (but not to all printers), it is necessary to consider whether the camera copy or line blocks for mathematics could be prepared from handwritten artwork.

In preparing the printer's copy, anything other than the simplest expression is best done by hand. Few typists possess extensive mathematical knowledge, and much time can be wasted trying to achieve the correct result on a typewriter. Also most typewriters (other than some 'golf ball' machines) provide only one size of type, so that proper setting of superior and inferior indices is not possible.

The appropriate British Standards covering mathematical notation and preparation of mathematical copy should be used (*see* page 201). Although such publications may well form part of a working agreement with the printer, mathematical copy should be carefully prepared with a view to reducing author's instructions to the minimum. It is best to eliminate the need for all but essential instructions, by setting out the copy in a manner which will be unambiguous, even to a person who has no knowledge of mathematics. Where necessary a symbol should be identified by quoting a page and item in the relevant British Standard.

Mathematical expressions to be integrated into lines of text should, if possible, be presented in such a way that they may be set using the conventional keyboard setting, thus avoiding the need to insert extra space above and below. Some examples are as follows:

Avoid root bars. The square root of 12 should be written $\sqrt{}12$, and not $\sqrt{12}$, which may necessitate hand work. This also applies to bracketed expressions, thus $\sqrt{}(x + y + z)$.

Where any fractions required are not all available in the fount in the traditional numerator/denominator style, thus $\frac{1}{2}$, $\frac{5}{8}$, consideration could be given to showing all fractions using the solidus, thus 1/2, 5/8. Alternatively, use all decimal notation, for example, 0.5; but remember the '0' at the left of the decimal point where the expression is less than unity.

With superior and inferior indices, the index should be written, in its superior or inferior position, in a size smaller than the symbol it qualifies. Where the indices are not numerical but letters, the printer should be consulted as to the most economical presentation which is practical and acceptable.

When using the Greek alphabet, upright or inclined characters should be specified, with the name of the character written out as a note to the printer, thus, 'Greek l.c. omega', the first time it appears. Greek characters should not be significantly smaller than roman characters and arabic numerals.

Make a clear distinction between capital and lower case letters, especially when they have the same outline, for example, C and c, K and k. Where necessary a symbol should be marked up as a capital. This will also assist the proof-reading (*see* page 159).

A common cause of incorrect setting, which can be avoided, is the vertical alignment of the various expressions. A horizontal line should be drawn in a colour different from that used for the copy (for example, feint blue) and a note to the printer should state that this is the datum around which all expressions are to be set. Usually the horizontal line in a plus or minus sign can be used. The coloured datum line is shown as a broken line in Figure 8.1.

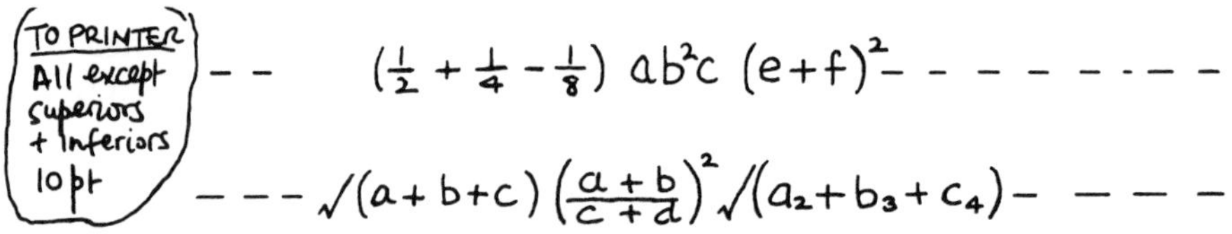

$$\text{[TO PRINTER: All except superiors + inferiors 10pt]} - - \quad \left(\tfrac{1}{2} + \tfrac{1}{4} - \tfrac{1}{8}\right) ab^2c \ (e+f)^2 - - - - - - - -$$

$$- - - \sqrt{(a+b+c)} \left(\frac{a+b}{c+d}\right)^2 \sqrt{(a_2+b_3+c_4)} - \ - - - -$$

Fig. 8.1   *Setting mathematical expressions.*

Spelling   Where spelling is critical, for example words to end in '-ize' and not '-ise', or where a particular spelling is required, the printer should be advised to spell as in the copy, and not refer to his house rules. Although requirements such as '-ize' could be a standing instruction, any individual words or exceptions to the rule are best marked up; this will also serve to guide the proof-readers. Note that '-ize' and '-ise' are not interchangeable on all words; if there is doubt refer to the dictionary.

Check Lists   Before requesting a first or galley proof, any check lists used in preparing the printer's copy should be examined to confirm that everything has been completed satisfactorily, and has been signed off.

PREPARATION AND PROCESSING OF ILLUSTRATIONS AND ARTWORK

Reference material, together with guidelines on production methods and the use and relative merits of the various types of illustrations are discussed in Chapter 4. This section will, therefore, deal only with matters of a general nature, and be complementary to Chapter 4 and the other technical chapters, for example, Chapter 7.

Originals suitable for reproduction by photolithography and photoengraving fall into two main groups: line and tone. Pen-and-ink drawings, scraper board originals, technical illustrations, engineers' plans and reproduction proofs or filmset letter-images of type matter are usual subjects in the first group. Photographs, pencil drawings, monochrome or coloured paintings and photographic transparencies are typical tone originals.

Ideally, for completed jobs to be satisfactory, all graphic reproduction processes need a very good original. Sophisticated techniques performed by experts can often reduce imperfections by skilful retouching, but an artist retouching without proper concern for technical accuracy can run into trouble. In any event, the only true criterion for gauging the efficiency of a reproduction process must be the degree of fidelity of a finished print to the original.

The preparation and development of illustrations is very much the concern of both author and editor, and no significant changes from the author's 'roughs' should be made without agreement. Artwork preparation is expensive, and care should be taken not to depart significantly from the original without referring back. At worst, complete redrawing may be required, which could not only affect the budget, but also upset the timetable. The processing of artwork is also dealt with in the appendix to this chapter (*see* Timetable).

Line Illustrations   Line work should preferably be drawn to a size larger than the proposed print (normally a ratio of 3:2 or 2:1 will be the most economical). As well as simplifying the artist's job where very small and detailed reproductions are concerned, provision of oversize originals means that photographic reduction will tend to conceal any minor faults in them. Maximum contrast in line drawings is a prime requirement, and is best achieved by drawing with process black ink on a smooth white surface free from yellow or brown undertones. All lines must be solid black and firmly drawn, otherwise they tend to fill in or become spoiled in some other way when reproduced.

For photoengraving, the thinness of lines on the original should be watched, and should be related not only to the photographic reduction but also to the material to be used for the block.

Where the photolithographic platemaking process is electro-static, drawing to the print size will eliminate the need for photographic reduction of the original.

Tone Illustrations   Where a line illustration is not to be used, a photograph will have to be obtained or commissioned. Most manufacturers are aware of the publicity resulting from the reproduction of pictures of their products, and will usually supply good quality photographs in return for an acknowledgement in the publication.

Where an original photograph has to be taken, it is important that the subject matter be photographed from the viewpoint best related to the associated text.

Processes   The type of negative required will vary according to the platemaking technique:

(a) For litho platemaking, either a photographic negative or positive will be required by the platemaker. The former will show the eventual printing image as transparent against an opaque black ground of non-printing area, whereas in a positive the image is black on a transparent ground. Any faults in a negative or positive must be retouched manually before platemaking, and the opening up of lines or the reducing of dots carried out by the chemical process of reduction.

(b) For photoengraving, a photographic negative will be required.

For either process, where a photograph is required it should be unglazed, and made on glossy bromide paper and have a neutral black image with a good soft tonal range. Normal key photographs are quite satisfactory; while high key photographs (that is, those where the tones are mainly at the lighter end of the print scale) reproduce well in lithography.

Instructions to Artist   The author's 'roughs' should be examined for ambiguity, especially in those parts of the drawing where detail is important. Normally, author and editor will have spent some time refining the roughs in the course of preparing the text, but because the artist is sometimes expected to work from a photocopy twice or three times removed from a poor original, a further check is not out of place. Also, no artist can be assumed to have a detailed knowledge of every subject.

Special attention should be paid to the precise termination of indicator lines (some with arrow heads and some with blobs) and their associated captions, which should conform to any conventions governing the use of capitals only, or a mixture of capitals and lower case lettering.

Any notes written directly on the rough should be annotated 'TO ARTIST' and ringed to distinguish them from copy. The artist should be advised of at least the following.

(a) The platemaking process and material (photoengraving – zinc, photolithography – electro-static).
(b) Any special points where precision of detail is essential.
(c) The proposed published size of the illustration and lettering.
(d) Whether the illustration will be viewed portrait (with its vertical parallel to the spine of the document) or landscape (with its vertical at a right-angle to the spine).
(e) Whether mechanical tints (representations of hatching, shading, etc., pre-printed on a transparent ground) may be used.
(f) Whether colour is required, together with the form of the artwork to suit the colour printing process.

Clearing the Artwork   Artwork should be checked as carefully as the text; too often, it is just 'looked at'. A safe way to work is to have a photocopy of both the rough and the artwork, then, starting at the top left-hand corner of the rough, work from left to right in strips, ticking off the detail and wording on both as they are cleared. This will show up anything which has been missed. This check should be separate from any other checks.

Corrections (which should first be agreed in consultation with the author, as some 'errors' may be acceptable to him) should be marked on the transparent overlay. This can, if necessary, be supplemented by a separate sheet, so long as it is clearly related to a note on the overlay. Care should be taken not to damage the original when writing on the overlay; a sheet of clear film should always be interposed between overlay and original.

Instructions to Printer   Precise instructions to the printer should accompany all originals; these can be conveniently indicated on a transparent overlay. Such matters as size of reproduction, screen rulings, mechanical tints, etc., should be covered.

Where special quality of reproduction is required, screen rulings and angles, platemaking processes and materials, paper quality and the printing process, would best be agreed in consultation with the printer.

PROOFS AND PROOF PROCESSING

This section covers the various stages of proof checking, including the arrangement of the text, illustrations, tables, headings, etc., in their final form.

First or Galley Proof Unless there are standing arrangements, a specific number of first proofs (or an appropriate number of copies of the potential camera copy) should be requested. These should be marked 'PROOF ONE', preferably on every page. Normally, first proofs will not be separated into pages or have illustrations and tables in position. One proof will be required for each of the following processes: proof-reading; proof checking; entering proof readers', checkers' and other corrections (the 'Working Proof'); marking up for the printer to prepare a second (or page) proof. Further copies may be required for author, etc. If all previous stages have been completed in accordance with a proper system, there should be no further need for author participation once the final text has been agreed. The temptation to reword or rearrange is best not presented to the author; author's corrections can be very expensive, and prevention is better than cure.

Proof-reading Although it may sound extravagant, both proof-reading and checking of the drafts are, except in obviously simple cases, best done by two people, and, if possible, should exclude the typist, author and editor.

Proof-reading, to be valid, must be done by responsible and suitably qualified personnel, to a set of simple rules. Firstly, the proof-readers must be able to spell, and have enough sense to know when to refer to a dictionary. Secondly they must be provided with accommodation in which they will be able to maintain concentration while working. Thirdly, they must be given precise instructions on what they are to check, for example, just the text, and not such things as bold types, layout and indents, etc.

Before starting work, the copy should be checked for completeness by referring to the page numbering system. Any blank spaces not annotated accordingly should be reported.

One proof reader should read aloud from the copy, while the other checks the words on the proof (when checking drafts, never the original, which should have been put away for preparation of the next stage).

It is not sufficient for the person reading aloud to read only the words, all punctuation and other marks must be included. Thus the printed passage:

> The out-of-date records have been placed with Her Majesty's Records Office (HMRO), 'for the sake of good organization', as a spokesman put it, with the following exceptions:

would be read aloud as:

> *Cap* The out *hyphen* of *hyphen* date records have been placed with *cap* Her *cap* Majesty *apostrophe* s *cap* Records *cap* Office *bracket caps* HMRO *close brackets comma quotes* for the sake of good organization *spelt with a z close quotes comma* as a spokesman put it *comma* with the following exceptions *colon*

The person checking the words on the proof should imagine the proof as having a vertical line down its centre, and should mark the corrections in red ink (never black) in the right- or left-hand margin, as appropriate. The corrections should comply with the appropriate British Standard (*see* page 201).

Proof-readers should confine their efforts to finding and noting errors in the proof. They should never fail to indicate a difference between the proof and the copy, even though the difference may appear to them to make sense. In such instances they should either correct the proof in accordance with the copy, or, where this could be unduly laborious, make a marginal note drawing attention to the differences, so that a decision may be taken at the proper level.

Proof-reading should not be combined with any other checks on the proof; these should be done separately.

The proof-readers should take turns at reading and checking (15 minutes each is reasonable). The person reading aloud must always read from the printer's copy. Concentration is proportional to the entertainment value of the text; a spare parts catalogue will obviously be more tiring than a novel. Generally, it can be assumed that a rest should be taken after one hour.

A test of concentration is for the person reading aloud to introduce a deliberate mistake at judicious intervals. Experience will show how long it takes for enthusiasm to be restored.

Where the proof-reading activity is parallel to other work on the proofs (such as checks on typography, layout, etc.) the timetable for these other tasks could be used to give the proof-readers the maximum possible breaks between sessions.

With experience, various ways can be devised to reduce the tedium of proof-reading, for instance, instead of announcing a capital letter each time one occurs, it can be indicated by tapping with a pencil. Where other refinements occur frequently in the text, for example, hyphens, these could be indicated by sliding the pencil over a roughish surface at the appropriate time, and so on.

Where the drafting and equipment used has resulted in potential camera copy from the start (cut and stick, word processor) advantage can, of course, be taken of any proof-reading which remains valid from draft to draft. The checks to be made on unchanged text from word processors must be related to experience but verification that all paragraph masses have been reproduced, would probably be a prudent minimum.

Proof Checking   As well as reading, other checks will have to be made on the proofs. Suggested items for inclusion in a check list to be applied at this stage are given in the appendix at the end of this chapter.

Once checks have been completed by all concerned, the corrections and suggestions from all sources should be consolidated on to the working proof. Printer's errors should be marked in red. Anything other than a printer's error should be marked in another colour (never black) and its source indicated.

The co-ordinator should review the working proof, should eliminate any corrections or suggestions he considers unnecessary, and should ensure that all instructions to the printer are either in accordance with the British Standard or are unambiguously indicated by 'Notes to Printer' (*see* page 154). The final corrections may then be entered on the corrected proof for printer, with an advice to the printer that 'author's corrections' are indicated in such a colour.

Page Make-up   Where the printer's proof or potential camera copy is acceptable, the page make-up should now be finalized, and the text, illustrations, tables, running heads, shoulder headings, page (folio) numbers, etc., should be marked up to show the position they should occupy on each page in the publication's final form.

It is best to prepare a separate page dummy for the right-hand (usually odd-numbered) and left-hand (usually even-numbered) pages. The dummies should show the maximum image area, the position of chapter numbers and titles, running heads and shoulder headings (q.v.), position of page number and any other features specific to the publication. A specimen dummy for a right-hand page is shown in Figure 8.2.

Using the dummy and either the working proof, or one of the other used proofs, the width of the image area should be checked (this is unlikely to vary unintentionally) and the chapter (or separate batch) should be marked off provisionally in units of the image area length (not forgetting footnotes).

Tables and illustrations, or, where they have still to be let into the text, their allocated spaces and locations, should be checked for size and position. Tables and illustrations are best located on the same page as the associated text, or on the right-hand page which faces it. It is worth spending time trying to achieve the optimum position, especially with instructional and textbooks. Sometimes, cutting and sticking a used proof (or a photocopy of one) will, after a few pages, show how space may be found or lost, by re-positioning, and, where there is no alternative, by increasing and decreasing the space between paragraphs and around the tables and illustrations themselves.

Once the page make-up in relation to tables and illustrations has been settled, the text at the provisional page marks should be read to see if it can, sensibly, be broken at that place. There are a few special points to watch.

- A break in the text between a left-handed and a right-handed page (where both are on view) may be acceptable, but not vice versa, if this can be avoided.
- The flow of a complicated sentence may be ruined by a break from right-handed to left-handed page.
- A page or column should never end with a hyphenated word, or with a complete expression, for example, '100 kg (220 lb)', broken.
- Where possible, the preamble covering several sub-paragraphs should be on view with at least one of the sub-paragraphs.
- Special effort should be made to keep the whole of a mathematical expression and its key (for example, '$(a + b)^2$, where, a ... kg ... is weight: b ...') in view, without the need to turn pages.
- Blank pages required to produce a right-handed page, or to enable all folding and collating to be done by machine, should be indicated. Where pages are intentionally left blank to avoid hand work, or for any other reason, overprinting accordingly may be desirable. The multiples for machine folding, etc., depend on how many pages are imposed (arranged for printing so that they will read consecutively when the printed sheet is folded). When in doubt, the printer can advise on the paging which will obviate the need for hand work.

When specified, running heads (or headlines) are centred at the top of each page. Usually they repeat the book title on the left-hand page, and the chapter title on the right-hand page. In technical documents, especially those with many different sections (as in a maintenance manual) it

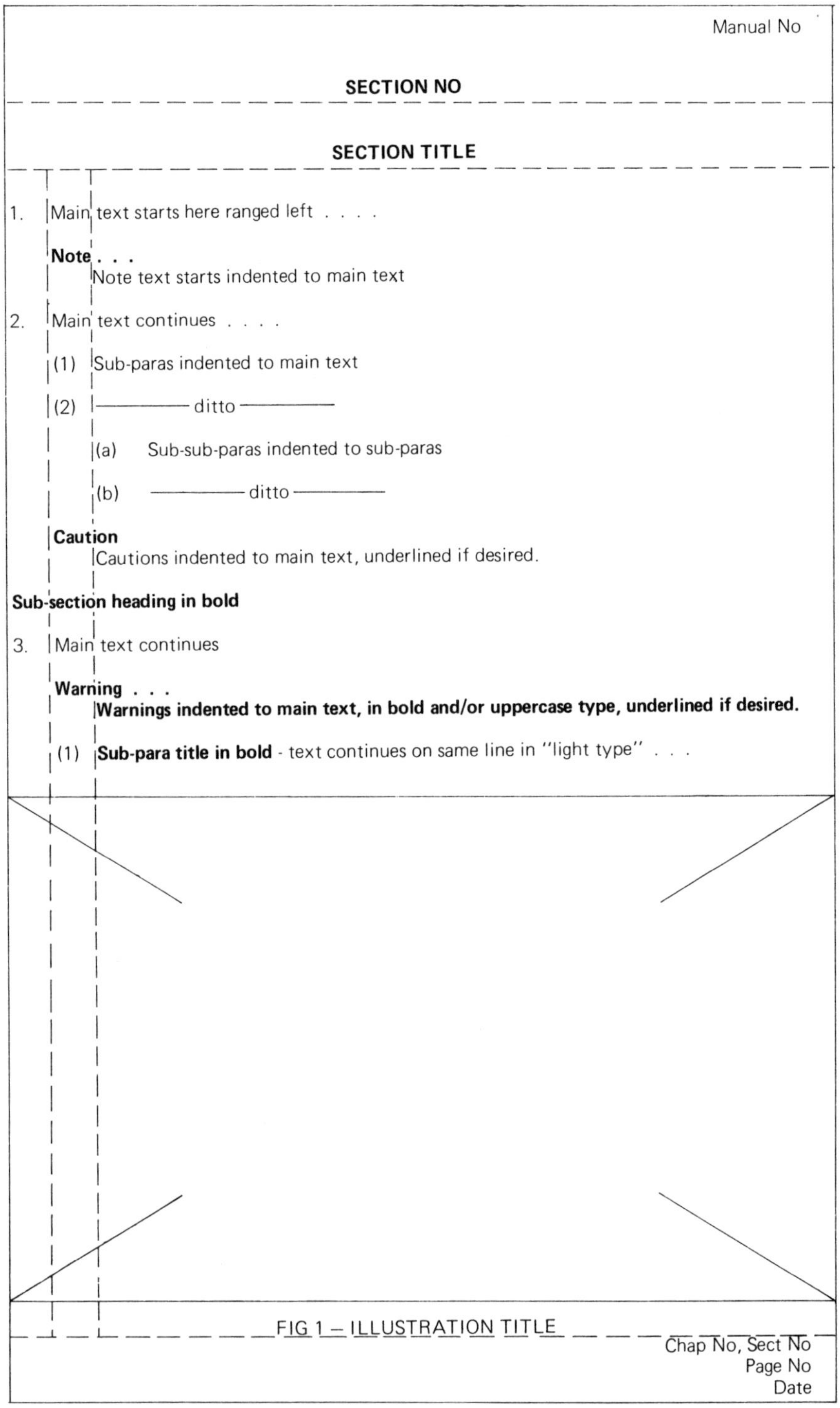

```
                                                          Manual No

                          SECTION NO
- - - - - - - - - - - - - - - - - - - - - - - - - - - - - - - -

                         SECTION TITLE
- - - - - - - - - - - - - - - - - - - - - - - - - - - - - - - -

1.   Main text starts here ranged left . . . .

     Note . . .
          Note text starts indented to main text

2.   Main text continues . . . .

       (1)  Sub-paras indented to main text

       (2)  ——————— ditto ———————

            (a)   Sub-sub-paras indented to sub-paras

            (b)   ——————— ditto ———————

     Caution
          Cautions indented to main text, underlined if desired.

Sub-section heading in bold

3.   Main text continues

     Warning . . .
          Warnings indented to main text, in bold and/or uppercase type, underlined if desired.

       (1)  Sub-para title in bold - text continues on same line in "light type" . . .
```

FIG 1 — ILLUSTRATION TITLE

Chap No, Sect No
Page No
Date

Fig. 8.2   Proof checker's page layout dummy.

may be more helpful to the user to give additional information; the normal running heads being dispensed with and separate headings (sometimes known as shoulder headings) being put at the right-hand and left-hand extremities at the top of each page. The most important information (the primary reference) should appear on the outside edge of each page. Thus, where the chapter number and title are the primary reference, the headings on a left-hand page would be arranged as follows:

CHAPTER 3   DISMANTLING
CARBURATION   FITS AND TOLERANCES

For a right-hand page, as follows:

SERVICING   CHAPTER 3
RE-ASSEMBLY   CARBURATION

Final or Page Proof   Before requesting the final or page proof, any check lists used in processing the first or galley proof should be examined to confirm that everything has been completed satisfactorily, and is signed off. Where the first proof was not good enough to warrant a page proof, page make-up should not have been attempted, and the corrected proof should be marked 'Revise' and signed, whereupon the printer should correct and submit another proof. If the first proof was good enough to warrant a page proof, the corrected proof should be marked 'Revise and make-up' and signed, whereupon the printer should correct and submit another proof in page form, with all tables and illustrations in position.

Suggested items for inclusion in a check list to be applied at this stage are given in the appendix to this chapter.

When a final page proof is available, the acceptability of the material for press should be established. Where the job has been planned and executed in accordance with a proper system, there should be no doubt about the quality of the material at this stage. All queries should have been eliminated or resolved *en route*.

When the proof is good enough to print it should be marked 'Press' and be signed. Where it is not desired to proceed until a perfect proof is available, the proof, with the printer's agreement, could be marked 'Correct then Press', and arrangements made for any corrections to be cleared at the printer's establishment, or alternatively given over the telephone. Often by this stage, despite planning, time is running short and some expedience is necessary in order to stay on schedule.

POST PUBLICATION

Details of procedures which may be found desirable following publication are given in the following appendix.

APPENDIX: TIMETABLES, CHECK LISTS AND INDEXES

INTRODUCTION

Check lists, timetables and the responsibilities for applying them will have to be related to the relative importance of each job, the internal procedures for drafting, editing, vetting, etc., and to the reliability of the personnel involved. If a person nominally responsible for the consistency of certain matters leaves much to be desired, it is common sense to arrange for separate cover, even though this may result in some duplication of effort. Such cover is also useful for drafting done on an occasional basis by members of senior staff, who cannot be expected to memorize and apply rules for isolated occasions.

Check lists themselves should complement house rules, and should be limited to matters requiring special attention in order to exercise quality control. All concerned should work against a common background of a specific dictionary (of the same edition), the British Standards appropriate to the subject and the *The Oxford Dictionary for Writers and Editors* with the check lists acting as an *aide-mémoire* for 'important' things, some of which may not be covered in the reference documents.

Items to be included in check lists will be suggested by subject matter, style and the need for consistency, especially in large publications or over long periods of time, where publications are amended in loose-leaf or loose-chapter form. With experience the lists can be reduced to key words, with amplifying material kept separately for refreshing the memory or for the training of new personnel.

For reference purposes, a master set of the current check lists, each identified by a reference number and date should be kept. The specimen timetable is so marked in the bottom left-hand corner. Out-of-date check lists should be made unusable as such, or destroyed.

Check lists should be signed off as processing the drafts progresses. Where necessary, a list of page numbers can be attached to the check list, and ticked and signed off at the end of each session, enabling another person to take over at any time and see what has been done. Where a job is separated into sections or chapters, a separate check list for each is advisable.

Obviously, check lists should never be treated lightly; an understandable temptation when the work being checked is near perfect. However tedious they may appear to be, they are the only means whereby consistency can be maintained over long periods of time, as regardless of staff changes, emphasis remains directed at those matters important enough to receive consistent treatment.

TIMETABLE (PUB 1)

The specimen timetable (PUB 1) covers 21 weeks (*see* Figure 8.3), and takes over when the drafting, commenting, agreeing, etc., has resulted in the production of the agreed text. The periods of time for each task may be modified, of course, to suit work loads. In the example, the parties involved are the publishers (PUB), printer (PRI), artist (ART) and distributor (DIS), all of whom may be within the same organization.

Note that 'artwork' (the drawings and illustrations which will be printed) is commissioned very early, once it is agreed in its draft form (roughs); it does not wait for agreement of the final text before being sent to the artist for preparation.

If the schedule has not already been agreed with the printer (for example, a regular biannual June and December job) the 'send copy to Printer' date (end of week 4) should be agreed with the printer at the earliest possible stage, preferably during the drafting stages.

The drafting stages (PUB 2) leading up to the agreed text have to be accommodated before the start of the publication timetable – so drafting may need to start up to 12 months before the planned publication date.

JOB: Publications Handbook

TIMETABLE FOR PUBLICATION BY: 18th July 1983

TEXT			ARTWORK
TASK	Week No.	DATE	TASK
Recieve final text, apply Check List PUB 3, prepare Printer's copy *(P U B)*	1	4/4	(a) Recieve artwork from Artist. (prepared before Week No.1) (b) Check against artwork roughs (c) Check against final text (No changes of captions etc) *(P U B)*
	2		
	3		
Send copy to Printer	4	29/4	(d) Send corrected artwork to Artist
Prepare galley proofs *(P R I)*	5	2/5	Correct artwork *(A R T)*
Send proofs to Publisher	6	13/5	Send corrected artwork to Publisher
Recieve galley proofs, apply PUB 4 to produce corrected proof and mark for pagination *(P U B)*	7	16/5 20/5	Recieve corrected artwork. Check. Send corrected artwork to Artist *(P U B)*
	8	23/5 27/5	Correct artwork and send to Publisher *(A R T)*
Send corrected proof to Printer	9	3/6	Recieved corrected artwork and send to Printer with instructions *(P U B)*
Correct proof, prepare page proof *(P R I)*	10	6/6	
Send page proof to Publisher	11	17/6	
Recieve page proof, apply PUB 5 Send corrected proof to Printer *(P U B)*	12	20/6 24/6	
Printer correct proof. Publisher clear for press. Print *(P R I)*	13	27/6	
	14		
Advance copy to Publisher	15	15/7	
Distribution *(DIS)*	16	18/7	
Post-publication procedures Check List PUB 6 *(P U B)*	17	25/7	Post-publication procedures
	18		
	19		
	20		
	21		

PUB 1
011283

Fig. 8.3   Specimen timetable.

Weeks 1–4 During this time PUB 3 is applied, and the printer's copy is marked up to ensure that the printer understands exactly what to do. Every item on PUB 3 is applied to every page, where appropriate using the 'style of the house' manual as a guide. This manual should specify how things are to be done so that all publications are consistent, for example, SI units are shown '10 kg (22 lb)', decimal points '1.5' and so on. The copy is sent to the printer with the date for proofs on the order (the number of proofs should also be specified).

Weeks 7–9   On receipt of first proofs the check list on PUB 4 is applied. The proof (corrected in accordance with the British Standard) is returned to the printer by the end of Week 9 with a request for second or page proofs with corrections and artwork incorporated. Note that the final artwork (following the right-hand side of the programme) should now be ready for photolithography or photoengraving and fitting into the page proofs.

Week 12   On receipt of final page proofs the check list on PUB 5 is applied and if artwork is the responsibility of a different person, is passed to that person. The final corrected proof (which ideally should need no further correction) is returned to the printer at the end of Week 12.

Week 16   The printed publication is received from the printer (any final corrections having been cleared by, or with, the printer before printing started) and distributed.

Week 17 onwards   The post-publication checks on PUB 6 are completed.

It is important that all concerned are aware of the timetable and have been warned in ample time before they are needed to do anything.

In some cases, especially for large jobs which may be split up into separate sections, batches or chapters, it may be advantageous to have a sheet complementary to the timetable on which actual dates and the progress of each item can be recorded. All that is needed is the job identification details and column headings covering the various parts of the timetable, 'Item', 'Final Text Received', 'Copy to Printer', etc. The columns can then be squared off and the dates entered in the appropriate squares. Red ink may be used to indicate an item which is behind schedule.

CHECK LIST FOR PREPARATION OF EARLY DRAFTS (PUB 2)

Matters of grammar, syntax, logical presentation, etc., will, normally, have been covered by the editor, who may have his own check list (*see* Chapter 5). The check list at this stage should be related to consistency, and the following items would form the basis of such a check list (PUB 2 in the text amplifying the detail on the Specimen Timetable).

Completeness of copy: No pages missing.

Layout and margins: To conform to style or separate dummy.

Running heads and shoulder headings: Accuracy and correct position relative to right- or left-hand pages.

Paragraphs: Agree with main heading. Agree with subsidiary heading. No duplication of headings under same main heading. Where there is a numbering system, all paragraphs numbered, and sequence of numbers in accordance with the convention (for example, one digit, two digits, three digits, letters of the alphabet, roman numbers).

Footnotes: Correct page (related to text). Symbol and order of symbols (e.g. *, †, ‡, §). Rule above footnote. Any variation of margin in relation to main margin.

Notes other than footnotes: Position in relation to associated text. Any variation of margin. Any convention, for example, 'NOTE:'.

Page numbers: Position and style, for example, Ch 11 App 5, 1, 2, etc. Reversion to 1, for example, for loose chapters.

Illustrations and tables: Convention for titles and captions. Readability of captions. Legibility of superiors and inferiors. In tables, brackets for, and style of units, for example (1000 m) (1,000 ft): (10^3m) (10^3 ft): alignment of columns. Proximity to introductory text.

Definitions, standard expressions and abbreviations: Correctly stated, for example, Blow-off Pressure: turbo-propeller/turbo-jet: ft/sec^2: m/sec^2: m/s^2: N/m^2: lbf/in^2 (not p.s.i. or lb/sq. in): Correct punctuation, e.g. i.e.: etc., and etc.: DTD: BBC: HM the Queen.

Decimal points: Point on line as in 1.5, and not centred as in 1·5.

Formulae: The key presented in order in which the symbols appear, also in consistent form, thus 'where, x . . . kg . . . is weight', or 'where, x is weight (kg)'.

Hyphens: No unacceptable hyphenation at ends of lines. Correctly placed in compound expression, for example, 'out-of-date design', but 'the design is out of date'. Variation of line length and its effect on hyphens in copy.

SI units: Correctly stated. Any accompanying conversions correctly shown, for example, 1m (3.280843 ft).

Cross references: Correctly stated according to conventions, for example, 'Appendix to Chapter 11': 'Ch. 11 App.'. References to external publications, for example, a British Standard, Handbook, should also be checked.

CHECK LIST FOR PREPARATION OF PRINTER'S COPY (PUB 3)

As previously stated, errors are costly to correct once set. It is, therefore, vital that the copy be as free as it can be from error and ambiguity. The following items should be considered for inclusion in the check list (PUB 3 on Specimen Timetable) for the preparation of the copy.

Preliminary The final draft (the text for the copy) should be checked for completeness. The contents of associated job bags, folders, etc., should be checked, and any outstanding matters should, where necessary, be incorporated in the text or otherwise disposed of.

- The copy should conform to appropriate British Standards.
- The copy should be on one side of the page only, with pages of identical size.
- Each page of the copy should be numbered consecutively at the top right-hand corner, with the total number of pages in each batch entered on the first page. Any page numbering conventions should be observed, especially those relating to added or deleted pages.

Checks In addition to the items covered in the check list for the early drafts, the following should be considered for inclusion in the check list.

Layout or dummy: Attachment to copy.

Gaps: No unintentional gaps in copy.

Space for inserts: Unambiguous instructions concerning reservation of space for illustrations, tables, mathematics, etc.

Layout of mathematics: Practicality of layout in copy, if setting is required. Founts required. (Ref. to appropriate British Standard).

Spelling: Any special spelling indicated.

Type faces: Any change of type face and/or size for special purposes, for example, for long extracts from other documents, to give them added emphasis. Bold and italic type for special cases, for example, cross references, titles, foreign words and phrases.

Intelligibility of mark-up: The need for a second person to check the copy for ambiguities, etc.

CHECK LIST FOR CLEARANCE OF FIRST PROOF (PUB 4)

On receipt, each set of proofs should be checked for completeness and marking up as 'PROOF ONE'. Each set should be marked with its function, for example, Proof-Reader's, Working Proof, Corrected Proof for Printer. To be safe, the working proof and the corrected proof for printer should be so marked on each page. Rubber stamps can be prepared for the regular markings.

The following (PUB 4 on Specimen Timetable) should be considered for inclusion in the check list.

Typography: That correct founts, point sizes and line spacing have been used. This check should precede all others.

Proof-reading: The responsibilities of the proof-readers, for example, read and check text only; check margins for position and alignment, check hyphenations at line endings.

Titles and headings: That the correct typeface has been set, for example, 10 pt Gill Medium, 10 pt Times New Roman Bold. That the spelling is correct (a check separate from that done by the proof-readers). That punctuation is correct and makes sense as set.

Running heads and shoulder headings: The text for each page should be added when page make-up is decided. Typeface and location should be indicated remembering that positions change with right- and left-hand pages.

Left- and right-hand margins: These should be checked for accurate positioning; also for unintentional blank spaces. No complete expressions broken up at the line ends, for example, '100 kg (220 lb)'. No unacceptable hyphenation at line ends.

Figures, tables, formulae, numerical values: Where formulae and numerical values appear in the first proof, a check for accuracy, separate from that done by the proof-readers should be made. Also the proximity of figures and tables to associated text (or allowed space) should be acceptable. The allowed space should be accurate in both size and position.

Cross references: None is invalidated by page make-up or proof corrections. Where publications are interrelated and subject to updating, cross reference indexes will be necessary and these are dealt with later in this appendix.

Footnotes: Correctly placed relative to associated text, and correct sequence of marking (thus *, †, ‡, §).

Contents list: Marked up to agree with corrected proof, for example, titles, reference numbers (Issue 1 etc.), dates.

Mark-up: Printer's errors marked-up in red. Author's corrections (anything other than a printer's error) in another colour (never black).

Page make-up: Image areas. Optimum position of reserved spaces. Break in sentences between right- and left-hand pages. Intentionally blank pages, etc.

Intelligibility of mark-up: The need for a second person to check over the marked-up proof for ambiguities; practicality of mark-up when related to the typesetting process, etc. Also mark-up conforms to the appropriate British Standards.

Index: For a 'once-only' publication, the copy for the first proof of the index could be prepared from the marked-up proof which will now give page numbers. Where each paragraph is numbered, the index could, of course, be prepared at the same time as the other copy. Indexes for publications which are interrelated or which will be updated and amended, are dealt with in greater detail later in this appendix.

Where the first proof is not good enough for preparing a final or page proof, further proofs marked 'PROOF TWO' and so on, should be requested until an acceptable proof is provided. Any modification of the checking procedures would depend on assurances from the printer concerning which parts of the proof have been reset, and which parts have been corrected or amended. Even on text which has not been touched, it may be wise to at least check that all paragraph masses have been reproduced.

CHECK LIST FOR CLEARANCE OF FINAL OR PAGE PROOF (PUB 5)

On receipt, each set of proofs should be checked for completeness and marking-up in accordance with the correct consecutive number. Each set should be marked up with its function, as appropriate to this stage. The same precautions should be taken in marking the working proof and the corrected proof for printer.

The following (PUB 5 on Specimen Timetable) should be considered for inclusion in the check list.

Corrections on previous proof: Check that all corrections have been incorporated.

Titles of figures, etc.: Check that positions are still correct; check that title and its figure or table correspond.

Artwork (figures, tables, etc.): Check that artwork is nicely balanced in allotted space, with not too much spare space around it.

Page make-up: Check that page make-up is in accordance with instructions, or if otherwise, is acceptable. Check effects of changes on any contents list or indexes.

INDEXES FOR PUBLICATIONS WHICH ARE INTERRELATED OR SUBJECT TO AMENDMENT

Where an organization has several publications which are interrelated, or subject to updating and amendment, additional records are necessary. Consider a hypothetical Body as an example, where the following could apply:

- The terms of reference of the Body are set out in an Act of Parliament (AP).
- The Body causes to be published a Statutory Instrument (SI) setting out the law amplifying the AP.
- The Body publishes Acceptable Means by which Compliance (AMC) may be shown with the SI.
- The Body publishes Periodic Notices (PN) dealing with day-to-day matters, interpretations of AMC, etc.

All these publications could be subject to amendment, could be interrelated, and could cross-refer to one another. To cover these eventualities extra records in the form of indexes are required.

Index to the Index   When publications are amended and topics previously mentioned are either referred to in different places, or are no longer referred to at all, it is clearly necessary to update the index accordingly. Care should be taken to ensure that all the relevant references in the index are accounted for. Thus, if, say, AMC Chapter 11, Paragraph 3.1.2 which covers 'multinational oil consortia' were to be deleted, it would be necessary for the person revising the index to know (*a*) whether or not there were any references to 'multinational oil consortia' in the index, and (*b*) whereabouts in the index any such references appeared. It should not be assumed, for instance, that 'multinational oil consortia' would appear in the index only under 'M' for 'multi' – it could equally well appear under, say, 'O' for 'oil'.

Therefore, where publications are to be amended, an index to the index is needed, and one in the following form, covering every item in the index, would show where the entry occurred.

Index to Index AMC

Ref. is made to: AMC Ch 11, para. 3.1.2   *Under*   M O C
Such an entry would cover the following entries in the index –
(a) M – Multinational oil consortia .... Ch 11 para 3.1.2
(b) O – Oil consortia, multinational .... Ch 11 para 3.1.2
(c) C – Consortia, oil, multinational .... Ch 11 para 3.1.2

Cross reference Index   It is most important that the cross reference index (which should cover all documents referred to, both internal and external) should be properly maintained, as an out-dated cross reference could have serious repercussions. The cross reference indexes (one for each publication referred to) could be in the following form.

X – Ref. Index to SI

Ref. is made to: SI 4 (c) (iii)   *In*   AMC Ch 12, para 6.4.1
                                                              PN 24, para 3.

Thus if SI 4 (c) (iii) were altered, AMC Chapter 12, paragraph 6.4.1, and Periodic Notice No. 24, paragraph 3, could be examined to determine whether the cross references were still valid.

Where card indexes are used the cards should be stored in the numerical order of the reference referred to. Obviously the references can only be as precise as the presentation of the various publications allows. It is advisable, in legal and semi-legal documentation, to adopt a system whereby any publication and any paragraph in it can be accurately and definitively identified by a single reference, thus, AMC 11, 3.1.2.

Where a significant cross reference is out-dated, consideration should be given to the advisability of informing holders of the relevant publication of the new cross reference, so that they may make a manuscript correction if they wish to do so.

CHECK LIST AFTER PUBLICATION (PUB 6)

Following publication, action will be influenced by the procedures which are normally followed in the organization. The following (PUB 6 on Specimen Timetable) should be considered for inclusion in the check list.

Corrected proofs and copy: The corrected proofs and the copy should be returned by the printer.

Records: Records of each stage (where so desired) should be put away.

Folders: The working folders should be put away after being cleared of anything which is not required for record purposes.

Master copy: Any master copy of the document should be brought up to date.

Indexes: Any indexes (for example, Cross reference Index) should be updated.

Modifications: Any modifications to procedures or check lists as a result of experience should be incorporated.

Errata/corrigenda: An errata/corrigenda folder should be opened, so that any errors/corrections may be collected and sent out in economical batches.

CHAPTER 9

Technical Publications Equipment

by

P. GREENFIELD

Today there is available a variety of office equipment which not only makes the work of technical authors and illustrators less mundane, by allowing them to spend more time on creative and less on routine production work, but which also makes the technical publications department more efficient, both in production and archive.

The range of equipment is large and innovations and improvements are frequent; so when contemplating the purchase of such equipment a full manufacturer's demonstration should be arranged and all the possible uses explored. Nevertheless, the main types of equipment likely to be used can be broadly described here, and the relative merits discussed.

TEXT PRODUCTION EQUIPMENT

This is a general heading covering the range of equipment available to the author for producing, correcting and recalling his text. At all times the author should be able to amend, update, correct and edit his text with ease and speed; the correct equipment will enable him to do this.

Typewriters A typewriter is the most basic requirement for any technical author; it offers a standard identity for layout and typeface for a department, regardless of the originating author. An immense range of machines is available, offering a variety of facilities with prices varying accordingly.

The trend now is towards 'intelligent' typewriters, which means that the machine has some form of recall memory that enables the author to proof-correct the material as it is typed and make corrections without the need for retyping. Typically, a memory would be limited to 7,500 characters. These machines usually also have a buffer storage, which holds up to 8 characters, and allows the typist to type faster than the machine could normally print, while allowing the machine to produce type at an even speed. This typewriter would normally allow the choice of 10 or

12-pitch spacing plus a choice of type face; the more expensive machines would produce proportional spacing allowing each character to take the space it individually requires; some also offer right-hand justification.

An 'intelligent' typewriter would be more adaptable than a standard machine for a publications department as it will not only give the author a more flexible editing facility but can produce good quality reproducible copy. This type of machine, because of its flexibility, is slowly replacing the standard electric typewriter as well as the mechanical proportional and justifying type composers.

Advantages   A typewriter is an essential item of equipment; the 'intelligent' typewriter offers flexibility – it will allow the author to correct his first draft without retyping, it offers a choice of type face and spacing, and will produce quality typing suitable for reproducing and direct cutting of stencils and paper offset plates. It is compact, quiet and requires no operator training.

Disadvantages   The typewriter offers no storage facility, which means that once the author has corrected his work and it has been retyped, he can no longer change it without typing again. The work must be checked immediately after the initial typing or no other work can be typed, and no archive use is available. The machine offers no communication with any other piece of office equipment and cannot be added to if any further facility is required by an expanding department.

Relative costs   Cost will vary with the required facility, but that of an 'intelligent' typewriter would typically be twice that of an electric model with no intelligent facility, and at least one quarter the price of a very basic word processor (described below).

Word Processors   A word processor is more than just a 'very' intelligent typewriter. Used correctly it can become a time-saving device, a document storage facility, a preventer of final proof correction mistakes and an information processor. Again, there are many variations on the theme, and money will be the limiting factor on the machine's capabilities. A word processor is a mini-computer dedicated to the processing and storage of vocabulary, and a system would comprise a keyboard, visual display unit, storage and programming unit and a printer (*see* Figure 9.1). These four units can be separate or all in one; in most cases the printer is remote.

The keyboard is a standard 'Qwerty' style typewriter keyboard with additional keypads for text editing, movement of text, cursor movement, table organization, filing and retrieval.

The visual display unit (VDU) is a television screen which offers the operator a 'window' into the text at any chosen point; typically the window is equivalent to a half A4 area. The VDU allows the operator to organize layout before the text is printed.

The programming unit is known as the central processing unit (CPU) and contains the machine brain, memory and the disc drive units. This unit is the variable of the system; its power will depend on cost, and its size will vary from small units built into the VDU to small individual floor-standing units, up to computer-size units requiring their own room. There are two styles; a 'stand alone' where each screen has its own CPU, or a shared logic where several screens all use the same CPU.

The unit can be 'hardwired' or 'softwired'. A hardwired unit has the

Fig. 9.1   *Word processing system with single visual display unit, separate central processing unit and printer.*

program built into the electronics, and cannot be altered or updated. The softwired is programmed by the operator entering a program disc when the machine is to be used; the machine then stores this information in a temporary memory which will be retained while power is maintained to the machine. The advantage of this system is that the program can be updated and the machine's capabilities extended if required.

The actual documents are placed into the unit in similar fashion. The documents are stored on a 'floppy disc' either 5 inch or 8 inch diameter, made from a magnetic recording material. Some units use a compact cassette as the storage medium, although this lengthens information retrieval time. The documents are recorded and played back, like an audio tape. The disc normally holds an average of 200,000 characters, although machines using dual-density discs would double this, and the large separate systems mentioned could hold as many as 6 million characters. The CPU normally has two disc drives so that duplication of discs is possible.

The printer is a separate unit generally of 'daisy-wheel' style, although jet spray is available for the large systems. A wide selection of typefaces is available for these machines as is a choice of pitch and proportional spacing.

The printer would have a typical speed of 45 cps (characters per second), or 90 cps for a jet spray machine, and is used as a separate entity, that is, documents are printed while other documents are being typed. To facilitate this, printers can be fitted for continuous stationery or automatic single-sheet feed. To improve cost-effectiveness more than one word processor can share a printer.

Typically, word processors enable:

- editing and changing of the text, with automatic rearrangement of the original text to accommodate the new material;
- whole paragraphs to be added or changed;
- automatic justification of right- or left-hand margins, with character spacing effected over the complete line length;
- special page headings or footnotes to be kept in their proper positions at the tops or bottoms of pages, even though the adjoining text is rearranged;
- automatic breaking of long words;
- arrangement of the text so that long words are not split at the end of a page and the next page started with the second half of the word (this is termed 'protecting widows and orphans');
- searching for a word within a document;
- automatic changing of a word within a document;
- individual names and addresses to be typed on a standard letter;
- automatic page numbering (pagination);
- the selection of recto (right-hand) and verso (left-hand) tabs;
- automatic indexing, alphabetically or numerically;
- typing in columns, with updating either across or by snake movement;
- the protection of confidential areas of text;
- spelling checks within a selected vocabulary;
- automatic tabulation;
- changing of table columns without retyping;
- centring on tabs or on decimal points;
- the use of emboldened type by multi-striking characters;
- duplication of areas of text without retyping;
- automatic calculation of mathematical tabulations during updating.

The typical list given above could be greater or smaller, depending on machine design and cost.

Advantages   From the facilities listed above the advantages of a word processor system in a technical publications department are obvious. In addition the system can save time for the author, facilitate print liaison and improve the quality of draft publications; for urgent bulletins and circulars it can be the typesetting medium. The system will improve the updating of publications and make changes easier, quicker and thus more frequent. Also, as word processors are new technology, their design is based on system flexibility; so that additions and improvements can easily be incorporated in an existing system. Such a system, therefore, has a long life, which reduces long-term cost.

Word processors of different makes cannot communicate without an interface but, if necessary, systems can be made to exchange information. This can also be accomplished with other equipment such as computer, phototypesetters, telex equipment and telephone equipment, thereby making communication between other publication departments and print shops possible.

Disadvantages The main disadvantage of a word processor system is the cost. This can be retrieved by length and amount of use, but the return on investment of such a system is long term. To achieve full advantage of the system a word processor operator must be trained, although the system can be operated by a typist. Also, to gain full use of the facilities a person must be using the system all the time. Training is not only time-consuming for the operator, but also for the author who must understand the capabilities of an installation if he is to employ it to the maximum. Therefore, time must be allocated before a system is in full use. Manufacturers of systems provide comprehensive training, but generally a typist will need four months to become fully conversant with a system.

Word processors take up to 18% longer than a typewriter to program for initial text, so typing is slower and the error rate usually higher. Although the time is regained in editing and update, it means that office time must be re-allocated.

A word processor is not so reliable as a standard typewriter and when purchasing a system, service must be carefully considered. Experience has shown that the printer is the most unreliable part of the system, but normally input of information is not interrupted. However, a department has to learn to live with a word processor system.

Relative costs Idle time is, as with a computer, expensive – on an average 100 times more expensive than a typewriter – so the need for a system must be justified before purchase. If a department can justify a system, then costs can be recouped over a period of time. A system will cost as much as a department's mini-computer installation, but rental and lease agreements are available which would eliminate the initial outlay.

A final note: as first mentioned, a word processor is a dedicated mini-computer, and the larger systems become information processors. Departments dealing with many and/or long parts lists or frequently updated lists may need a larger system to handle the input, output and documentation of such information, and may find that a microcomputer would be desirable for the reliable archive of such information.

Photocomposers

A phototypesetting machine is not dissimilar to a word processor. It would not be a technical publications department item of equipment but would be a convenient ancillary facility in an associated print shop.

A phototypesetting installation produces direct transfer, camera-copy quality text for use on offset lithographic masters. The system has all the text setting facilities of a word processor, but the text production area is a camera which, using a film negative, produces text of various print typefaces; the operator can also select the leading (vertical spacing) required. The negatives available are of all the major recognized hot metal faces, available in sizes from 6 point to 72 point. Headline sizes are available depending on the system.

It is possible, via an electronic interface, for a word processor to exchange text with a photocomposer. This would mean that text checked and approved could be placed into the storage of a photocomposer ready for the operator to program the required typeface and size, thereby eliminating the need for proof correction of printed material. A photocomposer is a printing facility, but the advantage of such a machine being available to a publications department would be that all word processor

Fig. 9.2   *Typical technical publications phototypesetting system with four visual display units and a shared film processor which provides camera-ready copy.*

functions could be carried through to the final printed and published material.

A photocomposer is expensive and would only be suitable as an installation for full-time use by compositors in a print shop. (*See* Figure 9.2.)

TEXT DUPLICATION AND PRINT EQUIPMENT

This general heading is for equipment that could be used by a department to duplicate documents and books for draft, approval and translation. The equipment is intended for short-run duplication and not for final printed quality. It must be able to reproduce good quality at low cost, be easy to operate without specialist knowledge, and be compatible with the office environment.

Photocopier   This machine, the most generally used for office duplication, is quiet, clean to use, requires no master preparation and no operator training. The photocopier is used for very low quantity runs and will produce duplicates from all types of masters including text, half-tones and photographs. It cannot recognize colour very well, seeing contrast rather than having a colour response, and it cannot print in colour. Photocopiers can be placed in four categories, depending on whether they use a coated or a

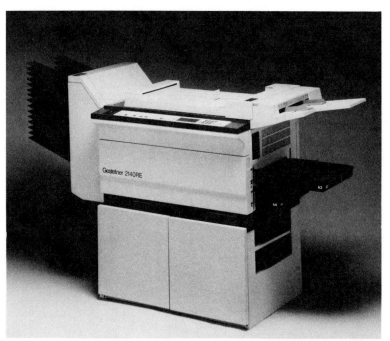

Fig. 9.3   Medium volume photocopier with document feed and sorter.

plain paper, or use a wet or dry developing system. The cheapest machines to purchase initially are those using a coated paper; often referred to as electro-static copiers, they produce a copy on a film-like paper. Reproduction quality is not high, the copy is sticky to the touch and likely to fade with time. Actual cost per copy is high as paper supply is expensive and they are only suitable for very low volume copying.

The plain paper type uses a permanent light-sensitive (generally selenium-coated) drum, which is electro-statically charged and then discharged by reflected light from the original. Toner adheres to the paper surface by electro-static charge. The term 'plain paper' is misleading because although any paper which accepts charge will make a copy, reliable copying can only be achieved from paper made specially for copiers. This paper is considerably cheaper than the coated variety and cost per copy is reduced. These copiers are by far the most common and range from table-top models aimed at a low volume and running from speeds of 10 copies per minute, to high-volume units running up to over 100 copies a minute and requiring special installation.

Wet toner machines are now on the decrease as although they are plain paper copiers they require high quality paper, are not so clean, and do not give high quality copying. The generally accepted office copier is now a plain paper, dry toner machine.

When purchasing a photocopier it is essential to match the copier with the volume of copying required. Recommended volumes will vary with manufacturer but generally, machines producing 12 copies per minute are suitable for volumes of less than 5,000 per month, 15 to 25 copies per minute for volumes between 5,000 and 10,000 per month and 25 to 60 copies per minute for up to 30,000 per month. Copier use will also depend on the average number of copies made per original. Copiers are generally selectable for making between 1 to 99 copies and will handle A4 to B4 sheets of paper, the more expensive handling up to A3.

Optional equipment may include a collator/sorter attachment and a document feed for automatic feeding of originals; these would considerably improve the speed for duplicating larger documents (*see* Figure 9.3).

Recent photocopiers now also offer reduction and enlargement facilities.

Advantages   The photocopier is a convenient, clean, adaptable and fast piece of equipment which can also produce transparencies and labels using special materials. It is most suitable for producing relatively small numbers of copies from any original, but it is the only piece of equipment which offers immediate duplication of almost any original without need for special preparation of the original. It can be used by anyone without training, and can be sited almost anywhere without intrusion into the office environment.

Disadvantages   The photocopier requires a relatively stable power supply and will be unreliable during power fluctuation. It requires regular servicing and is not as reliable as other duplicating machines; after purchase a service contract would be advisable. The copier can only produce black text copy, although certain large duplicating agencies do have plain paper copying machines with a limited colour reproduction facility. It is not generally suitable for copying on pre-printed paper and can only handle paper of weights between approximately 60 to 100 g.s.m. (grams per square metre).

Relative costs   Photocopiers are expensive compared with other duplicating machines but their ease of use and adaptability outweigh this. The cost per copy will vary depending on the type of machine but as a general rule they are not suitable and are extremely expensive for runs of more than 100 copies. The break-even quantity for copiers compared to other systems is approximately 25 copies.

Non-impact Printer   The non-impact printer is a further development of the photocopier, which has risen from a requirement to meet the printing needs of word processor and computer users who need several copies of the stored information.

The printer is basically a photocopier with the exposure and optics sections removed. The selenium or cadmium sulphide coated copier drum (the photo-conductor) is retained, and the image is produced and fixed on the paper in the same way as for a standard photocopier.

The photo-conductor is exposed by either light emitting diodes (LED) positioned in a specific array across the drum's surface, or by a helium–neon laser. Information is supplied, in digital form, from the word processor, and is stored in a built-in memory where it is used to expose the copier drum via the laser or LED. The image is then developed, by a method which is the reverse of that employed in standard copiers, and then transferred to the paper by the normal method.

An advantage of this type of printer is that, because information is held in a digital store, character generation can be programmed separately from the actual processed information. This means that the printer is capable of reproducing several different typefaces including foreign type characters and graphic symbols.

The printer can accept a wide range of paper and is extremely fast; the minimum rate is 60 prints per minute, printed continuously with no delay for page change over.

Although these printers are very expensive, further development and the increased use of word processors in technical publications combined with the printer's graphics capabilities may result in increasing use of such printers to produce complete proof copies or low quality technical manuals.

Duplicators   The title 'duplicator' can be given to two basic machines using totally different principles of operation, namely the stencil duplicator and the spirit duplicator. These machines offer duplication at a low cost per copy and very low initial outlay; but because both require the preparation of special masters, cost per copy, taking time into account, is high for low-volume runs.

The spirit duplicator uses a carbon master which is cheap, but which has to be individually prepared and which has only a short life.

The duplicator uses an ethanol-based fluid for duplicating; the copies will fade over a period of time. Spirit duplicators are cheap to buy and fairly easy to operate, but quality is poor and the machines now have a limited use for medium runs. The stencil duplicator is more versatile and is as common as the copier for office duplication (*see* Figure 9.4).

Stencil duplicators use a water-based ink, available in a wide range of colours. The stencils can be supplied in various types, choice depending on length of run required and how the stencil is to be cut. The process relies on the machine pushing ink through a cut stencil; originally these were of waxed paper, the wax being cut away to leave the porous paper. Most stencils now have a vinyl base, but very cheap paper-type stencils can be used for very low volume runs. Stencils can be cut by hand, typewriter or by a scanner.

What has made the stencil duplicator as versatile as the photocopier is the scanner, an electronic device which uses a photo-electric cell to scan

Fig. 9.4   *Fully automatic stencil duplicator with electronic scanner for stencil cutting.*

any original and convert recognized contrast and shade into an electrical spark to cut a stencil. A scanner can be fitted with colour separation filters for colour printing; and because it is a spark device it will change photographs into half-tones without the need for a dot screen.

The scanner allows stencils to be cut from any master with minimal preparation. The stencils suitable for electric cutting can be used for runs of up to 5,000 copies. Once the stencil has been cut the duplicator can run at speeds of between 50 and 150 copies a minute, depending on grade of paper. Machine speed will affect copy quality.

The stencil duplicator ranges from the simplest manual machine to sophisticated programmable models offering automatic stencil loading and ejection. The machines are easy to operate, reasonably clean to use and can print colour with acceptable registration. Print quality is equivalent to that of a photocopier.

Advantages   The singular advantage of a spirit duplicator is its low cost; however, a stencil duplicator is ideal for duplicating runs of more than 20 copies.

The stencil machine is a medium to low-cost machine that can duplicate at high speed and provides reasonable quality at a very low cost per copy – cost per copy reducing as more copies are taken, unlike a copier. It is small, can fit into any office environment, requires minimal operator training and has proved extremely reliable with little service necessary. It can print any colour required, feed paper of between 45 g.s.m. (Air Mail) to 180 g.s.m. weight, and can be operated manually in the event of a power failure.

Disadvantages   The spirit duplicator cannot provide a permanent copy, it produces only poor quality work, and is unsuitable for today's office environment. Both spirit and stencil duplicators can be noisy and require regular cleaning. Masters must be specially prepared, and can only be drawn, written or typed, unless a scanner is used to support the stencil machine.

Relative costs   Duplicators are of medium to low-cost in initial purchase. Masters can be relatively expensive to buy but this cost is reduced as more copies are taken from the master. Duplicators are not cost-effective for runs of less than 20 but cost per copy for runs of 100 and more is extremely low in comparison to photocopiers. For the stencil machine to equal a photocopier, a scanner must be purchased as part of the system; this will double the capital outlay and increase running costs.

Offset   The offset lithographic machine is a specialist print machine requiring a trained operator. However, the quality of offset and the ease with which plates can now be made have led to small table-top machines being marketed. Short-run paper plates can be made on certain photocopiers, or on specially converted photocopiers at very low cost, which means that small offset duplicators can be used in a similar manner to stencil duplicators.

The table-top offset printer (*see* Figure 9.5) is a medium-cost machine offering very low cost per copy on long runs – 100 or more – but high cost on short runs.

It can copy on to a wide range of paper, ranging from 45 g.s.m. to 290 g.s.m., and can print colour with good registration. The machines are

Fig. 9.5　Programmable table-top offset printer suitable for technical
publications use.

noisy and require special installation; also, additional platemaking equipment would be required.

An offset printer could be useful to a publications department with either very low quantity distribution or high quantity proof requirement, but otherwise it is a specialist print machine.

ILLUSTRATION PRODUCTION EQUIPMENT

This general heading covers equipment designed to aid the technical illustrator envisage artwork in layout form, reproduce a variation of the artwork or actually produce it. Machines in this group tend to have been designed for a specific purpose, rather than for general use which can be adapted to technical publication department needs, so comparison between systems is difficult.

Dyeline　A dyeline machine is a print machine used for line illustration artwork. It is really a drawing office machine and the only printer that can easily handle large sizes of paper. The master has to be on translucent material;

its print quality is not good enough for further reproduction; and only 'same-size' reproduction is possible.

The process, sometimes known as 'diazo', relies on the use of a special dyeline paper. This is coated with a special diazo compound, a pale yellow crystal of the diazonium salt group, which is neutralized when exposed to ultraviolet light. The process exposes the paper to ultraviolet light through the translucent master; when the paper is fed through developer, non-exposed areas turn either blue or black (depending on the developer used) and fuse.

The process can be used so that a copy of large artwork can be checked by the author and marked up, before inking the final original master, and without damage to the draft artwork. It can also reproduce second originals by using translucent plastic sheet coated with diazonium salt. Using this method, illustrators can produce a master which can be altered when further original artwork is required of similar subjects.

Paste-up Table and Lightbox These two items are used by the illustrator to organize and lay out the individual pieces that will make the page. The paste-up table is used for master artwork which will be made into plates, either by direct transfer from the master, or by an intermediate operation such as a negative. The lightbox is used for working on negatives or on reversal slides.

A paste-up table is a purpose-built drawing board fitted with a parallel movement for alignment of text and with adjustable rake for comfort. The table size will depend on the master format size, for example, tabloid or A0. The A0 size would be the most common in use for technical publications as these series of papers are ISO-recommended. The surface of the table can be fitted with grid overlays for layout guidelines.

A lightbox has an opaque glass working surface with fluorescent lighting mounted beneath (*see* Figure 9.6). This allows negatives to be laid

Fig. 9.6   Direct transfer processor unit, also suitable as lightbox for working on negatives.

on a table top and light to be shone through for ease of inspection; the illustrator can then work on the negative in the normal drawing position.

The illustrator would use the lightbox to remove from the negative any blemishes caused by spots on the positive or poor emulsion, covering them with photopaque, a mixture of china clay and ochre; also for stripping together several negatives to make one, using negative assembly tape or film; or for retouching reversal slides.

Cameras The camera is used to produce proofs, copy prints or plates and to view artwork in a reduced or enlarged size (*see* Figure 9.7). When used for platemaking the camera would normally be print-shop equipment, but it can be used in the technical publications department's photographic darkroom by illustrators.

A version of the plate camera can be adapted, by fixing a hood to the viewing area, for use under normal light conditions. The original artwork is placed on the baseboard and illuminated; then, by changing the relative positions of baseboard, lens system and viewing area, any size enlargement or reduction can be obtained. The projected image is viewed by placing a translucent film sheet on the top glass. The illustrator can then view the artwork in the predicted printed size, or trace an area of artwork in a different size.

The plate camera functions similarly, except that it is used in a darkroom fitted with a safe light. Once the camera operator has set the size of reproduction required, the photographic material is positioned on the viewing area then exposed as necessary.

The camera can be used to produce offset plates, negatives, copy proofs and direct transfer film.

The direct transfer process uses special chemicals and photographic materials to produce artwork in positive form without using an intermediate stage. Direct transfer is a cheap and quick method of producing prints,

Fig. 9.7 Typical reprographic camera for technical publications work.

as only one operation is needed and no negative material has to be purchased.

For greater convenience a direct transfer machine is available having the developer and fixer unit built into the exposure section, allowing 'same-size' artwork to be made into camera copy with no special installation required.

Computer Aided Design (CAD)   The technical illustrator has never relied totally on free-hand illustration, but has always used a drawing aid; this is also true for the production of lettering. Radius and ellipse guides, with stencils and dry transfer lettering, are long-established graphic tools. However, in the same way that technology has improved the author's lot so technology is now being used in the studio.

Computer aided design (CAD) originally began as a design drawing office aid but has graduated to three dimensional and perspective use, and has gained the title computer graphics.

CAD consists of a drawing board, with electronic sensors laid beneath the surface, and an electronic cursor which is moved over the board to input the design. This unit is connected to a visual display unit (VDU) and a computer which can calculate dimensions, amend screen input, input technical and specification data and store the board input.

To produce a drawing, the operator must produce a rough sketch using the cursor to trace the illustration and input the information. The input is then displayed on the VDU for checking, amending or adding annotations; and finally plotted using a pen plotter for hard copy. The information can be stored for display at any time, or for adding to further illustrations on a 'floppy disc' in the same way that information is stored on a word processor.

Computer graphics is a further extension of CAD and requires even greater computer capacity. The computer calculations required for drawing simple shapes like circles and ellipses are immense, and perspective illustrations make even greater demands. The main problem is in reducing the dot matrix that a computer must use, sufficiently for curves to appear smooth and continuous.

With full computer graphics it is possible to enter a design and turn it to view in any position required; enter a much-used design and incorporate it into a larger design at any time without redrawing; enter co-ordinates and construct a design within them; reduce or enlarge whole illustrations or areas independently; change colour and shade of areas, and experiment with designs easily and quickly without costly redrawing. It is also possible to store all illustrations within the memory, which reduces the storage normally required for large board-mounted illustrations.

The illustration can be copied for use as hard copy publication by either a pen plotter, or by feeding the information directly in digital form, to any type of controlled camera.

The use of CAD in a drawing office can also aid a technical publications department in other ways. As the complete record of machine drawings is stored within the system's memory, access to the memory for a technical author enables him to edit and produce documentation for spare parts. The information can then be printed on a 'daisy-wheel' printer or fed directly to a phototypesetter.

Graphic design by computer requires complicated input so consequently much of the input has to be made by keyboard, in addition to the electronic board and cursor. Computer aided design and computer graphic systems are large, complicated and therefore very expensive. For very large technical publications studios the systems could be cost-effective as they improve design capabilities and reduce time for repeat or similar illustrations; however, just as technology has reduced the cost and simplified the operation of other computer based systems such as word processors and phototypesetting systems, the same will eventually be true of computer graphics.

CHAPTER 10

Working with Technical Publication Specifications

by

MIKE AUSTIN

People engaged in producing engineering manuals and other types of technical document often have no freedom to choose the style that their work should adopt. They have to proceed within the confines of a publication specification issued by their employer, the customer or publisher for whom they are working, or some other omnipotent literary arbiter. Usually they will also have to comply with general specifications, such as those relating to SI units, abbreviations, or symbols for electrical diagrams, which apply across the whole spectrum of technical communication.

There are numerous publications specifications, and many are very comprehensive and complex; they are being continually updated, so it would be both impracticable and unproductive to try to explain their requirements in detail. Instead, I have confined myself to explaining the broad requirements of British Standard BS 4884, the basic standard governing technical manuals in the UK, and to showing how this standard can be adapted to suit particular requirements. I have also examined and compared typical requirements from four widely used publication standards – two military, one for civil aviation and one which governs power station publications.

Following this general review, I have given some advice that may help an inexperienced person faced for the first time with a specification of seeming mind-boggling complexity. I have also listed some of the more important general specifications.

BRITISH STANDARD BS 4884 – TECHNICAL MANUALS

As BS 4884 declares in its foreword: 'This standard applies to all documents which explain the use and maintenance of products, from the instructions supplied with a domestic appliance, written for the house-wife, to the total information supporting a complex system, written for the trained technician. Documents may vary in form from a small card to several volumes.' Unfortunately, the standard has not yet achieved the widespread use that its authors expected.

The standard is divided into two sections – Part 1 Content, and Part 2 Presentation.

Part 1 Content   Part 1 of BS 4884 lists and explains the following nine categories of information into which the details of a product may be divided, though not all of these will apply in every case.

Purpose and planning information   This category contains the information required to assess the product's suitability for a particular application and environment, and to forecast the support it will require. Essentially, it is intended to explain what the equipment is for, and to provide, especially for senior management, a quick reference as to its capabilities. Also included in this category, when applicable, are performance data, a list of associated reference documents and a statement of any associated conditions that could give rise to a hazard.

Operating instructions   This section contains detailed instructions for operating the equipment under normal and emergency conditions.

Technical description   In this category, the way in which the equipment works is fully explained both by text and illustrations. The level of background knowledge assumed will depend on the product and the circumstances. Obviously, one could assume that the staff of a power station would have a higher degree of technical knowledge than the reader of a car owner's handbook.

Handling, installation, storage, transit   In addition to the contents indicated by the heading, this category can include detailed instructions for initially setting up and commissioning the equipment.

Maintenance instructions   This section contains the detailed instructions for fault diagnosis, tests, checks, inspection and overhaul.

Maintenance schedules   The maintenance schedules list the maintenance tasks that have to be performed at specified intervals of time, distance, running hours or completed operations. Cross references can be made to the previous category for information on the detailed procedures to be adopted in order to carry out a scheduled task.

Parts lists   The purpose of this category is to enable the user to readily identify and obtain any spare parts he may require. The parts list should normally be illustrated, or reference can be made to suitable illustrations in other related publications.

Modification instructions   This category is provided as a location for modification instructions and special bulletins issued after the equipment has gone into service.

Disposal information   This category is most likely to be required when inherently dangerous substances are involved, and details any special instructions for disposing of the equipment or its components.

Part 2 Presentation Part 2 of BS 4884 gives general information on methods of presentation. Much of the information is given in the form of advice rather than as precise standards, but certain rules are laid down; for example, that margins should be not less than 20 mm. The type of information to be included on the front cover and in the title page and preliminary pages is listed, and a few specimen layout pages for text and illustrations are provided.

As BS 4884 is a general specification intended to apply to a whole gamut of products, from a domestic appliance to a ship, it can only provide general guidance in most cases, and serve as the foundation on which more detailed manual structures can be built. Two such derivatives will now be examined; the first is the Guide issued by the British Institution of Plant Engineers, and the second is the format of the manuals prepared in my own department.

TECHNICAL MANUALS – A GUIDE TO USERS' REQUIREMENTS

This Guide is aimed primarily at such people as senior management, works and maintenance engineers, buyers, designers, architects, contract managers and marketing executives. It is divided into three parts:

- Part 1 – contents and presentation.
- Part 2 – presentation techniques.
- Part 3 – publishing management.

Two appendixes to this Guide cover a list of reference books and a list of relevant British Standards.

The Guide recommends that the contents of a manual should be divided into eight categories; these are essentially the same as the first eight categories of BS 4884, as previously described. The information to be provided in these eight groups is expanded in directions likely to be especially relevant to plant engineers, and many examples are given of the types of illustration that could apply.

The presentation techniques described in Part 2 of the Guide follow the general pattern indicated in BS 4884, but contain more details, including such items as detailed page layout dimensions, annotation sizes and the size and style to be used for various headings.

Part 3 of the Guide briefly covers the management and organizational aspects of technical handbook production.

AN INDEPENDENT COMMERCIAL ADAPTATION OF BS 4884

In the technical publications department of HML (Engineering) Ltd we produce manuals on hydraulic test equipment for aircraft. Sometimes the customer requires that the manual should be to a particular specification; if not, we use our house standard, which is broadly based on the structure given in BS 4884.

We use all the categories of information listed in the standard, except for the last, which relates to disposal, and has no relevance to our equipment.

The order of the other eight categories has been rearranged as shown below, as this suits our requirements better. With this arrangement we can place the first five chapters into one volume and chapters six, seven and eight into another. Volume 1 contains the information most urgently required by someone receiving new equipment, and Volume 2, which takes more time to produce, can be issued later, without seriously interfering with the equipment's use.

Chapter
1 – Purpose and Application, and Data
2 – Operating Procedures
3 – Description of Equipment
4 – Preventive Maintenance
5 – Test Running Checks and Adjustments
6 – Corrective Maintenance (including description of individual components)
7 – Modifications and Special Features
8 – Illustrated Parts Catalogues

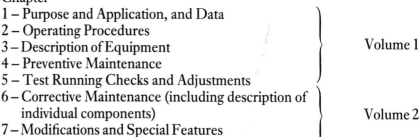

Volume 1

Volume 2

Many specifications, including BS 4884, create ambiguity in the way that descriptive information should be treated, because they do not differentiate between description of the complete equipment and description of its components. We regard it as very important that the description given in Chapter 3 of HML's manual should be restricted to that of the complete equipment or system (as required for the intelligent use and care of the complete equipment and system fault diagnosis); whereas the description of a component of the equipment or system (as required to diagnose faults in or to overhaul that component) is placed, where it logically belongs, as an introduction to the maintenance instructions for that component in Chapter 6.

These two fundamentally different categories of descriptive information can be well illustrated by an everyday example – the overdrive unit of a car. To use the car efficiently, it is useful to understand that the overdrive functions as an extra top gear, the appropriate use of which can reduce engine wear and fuel consumption. It is also useful to know that it works electro-hydraulically, and that there are operational limitations affecting its use, for example, a kick-down switch and another switch that prevents engagement at very small throttle openings. This is basic descriptive information useful to a driver and therefore suited to Chapter 3. But someone who only drives a car or carries out basic routine servicing does not need a detailed description of the overdrive unit including the hydraulic circuit.

The structure of the manual must take account of these two fundamentally different types of descriptive information. In the case of the overdrive, a full description of how it functions together with circuits and illustrations showing the construction of the unit should precede the detailed maintenance procedures in Chapter 6; because it is the maintenance man who, after the gearbox and overdrive unit have been removed from the car, will be using this information – not the driver, or a mechanic doing a general service.

Readers prefer this arrangement by which all the information on a component, such as a gearbox, is placed in one self-contained section, and it makes our life easy when the component is used again in another piece of equipment. The complete section can be repeated, with only a few minor corrections to the page heading, date and section number.

Chapter 4, Preventive Maintenance, details the procedures for carrying out the routine servicing tasks, as well as listing those to be performed periodically. Usually these jobs are quite simple, and it is essential that this information arrives early with Volume 1.

In Chapter 5 we include any detailed acceptance test procedures that may be required by the customer on receipt of the equipment; we also use this chapter for the special tests to be conducted after overhaul. By locating all the special tests in this chapter, they are kept clear of the normal operating procedures in Chapter 2.

Chapter 6, Corrective Maintenance, covers detailed fault diagnosis as well as the descriptive information and servicing procedures for each of the components – valves, pumps, gearboxes, etc. We use the terms preventive and corrective maintenance as these are self-explanatory and commonplace in the industry in which we work.

In addition to modification information, Chapter 7 is used to cover any non-standard special features incorporated in the equipment supplied to one customer only. It is usually much cheaper to add a special feature than to alter a standard chapter to cover a special case.

One of the most unpopular features of engineering manuals is the book that covers many variants of the equipment, without rigorously separating each variant. Some of our customers therefore insist that their manuals should contain nothing that does not apply to their equipment. This occasionally causes some headaches but I have quite a lot of sympathy for this demand. I, too, have been on the receiving end of such muddled books. To meet this requirement, to provide a flexible structure, and simplify amendments, we separate each chapter into several self-contained sections, with page numbers and illustrations starting at 1 at the beginning of each section. When a section does not apply to a particular variant of the equipment, we use a substitute page containing the words 'This section does not apply to the particular equipment covered by this manual'.

To cite an example – one of our standard test trolleys can have one of three different types of high pressure filter, according to the dictates of particular customers. In the Preventive Maintenance chapter, the instructions for each type of filter are detailed in a separate section. When collating the chapter we include the section covering the filter fitted to the particular equipment, plus two substitute pages for the sections not required. This is reflected in the chapter contents list.

When numbering the pages, we use the abbreviated words 'Chap' and 'Sect' in the form shown, as we find this less confusing to readers than the more common alternative form using only numerals.

Preferred Form	*Alternative Form*
Chap 6, Sect 11	6–11
Page 1	Page 1
May 82	May 82

Our illustrations are produced with the contemplation that they may be used in more than one manual produced to different specifications. We have therefore chosen a style and size that will meet most requirements. In practice, we find that the Ministry of Defence (Naval) requirements are the most stringent, and that an illustration drawn to this standard will fulfil most other needs.

BS 4884 (in common with many other official publications) uses the decimal system of paragraph numbering, although it does not actually state that this style should be used in manuals. We abhor this practice; it is ugly, confusing and a typographical nightmare. Imagine using it in trying to design an attractive sales brochure! The decimal system is especially misleading and undesirable when used for operating instructions, because it confuses what ought to be a clear distinction between an informative preamble and the mandatory step-by-step procedures which follow. Figure 10.1 shows some instructions arranged according to an official specification (upper) and the same instructions in a more attractive alternative form (lower).

COMPARISON OF FOUR WIDELY-USED SPECIFICATIONS

A broad insight into some of the main features covered by publications specifications can be obtained by comparing a number of typical items from the following four widely used specifications.

- AvP70, the Ministry of Defence specification for publications covering aircraft and associated equipment.
- DG Ships 607B, the Ministry of Defence (Director General Ships) specification for ship publications, prepared to joint services standards.
- Central Electricity Generating Board specification CEGB TP 30, for power station manuals.
- ATA 100 an international specification covering technical data for civil aircraft and associated airborne equipment, prepared by the Air Transport Association of America.

Page size and binding   ATA 100 specifies a standard page size of 8½ × 11 in. (American Quarto) with an oversize page of 11 × 16 in. for large illustrations. The other specifications prescribe A4 (210 × 297 mm) with A3 (297 × 420 mm) for the oversize (*see* Figure 10.2), All specify loose leaf binding, with a widely spaced two-hole binding for DG Ships 607B, a three-hole arrangement for ATA 100, and standard four-hole binding for the other two. Except for ATA 100, the binders are provided by the publication authority commissioning the manual.

Paper type and method of printing   ATA 100 gives broad guidance on both these subjects. In the other cases the printing is normally carried out by, or in conjunction with, the publication authority, although AvP 70 does specify the quality of paper to be used.

Dimensioned page layouts   Each of the specifications provides dimensioned specimen pages showing width of margins, position of page headings, illustration areas, position of page numbers and similar details.

Warnings, cautions, notes   The circumstances under which these are used are defined in each specification. AvP 70 and DG Ships 607B state that warnings must be printed in red, although in the case of AvP 70 this applies to full page warnings only.

Typing standards   In each case, instructions are included on the size and style of type, method of presenting headings and similar factors affecting presentation of the text.

Page numbering   Each sub-division in an ATA 100 manual has its own set of page numbers, arranged in a sequence based on chapter/section/

Bleeding the hydraulic system

13   After the trolley has been bled and preset (para. 11) it may be used to bleed the hydraulic system as follows:-

    13.1   Ensure that the trolley return pressure valve has been correctly set (para. 11.10) and that the pressure control valve(s) have been set to a suitable supply pressure (para. 11.9).

CAUTION . . .

    If the hoses are connected to the hydraulic system before setting the return pressure valve, the contents of the system reservoir will be discharged into the trolley tank, which probably will overflow.

    13.2   Connect the hoses:-

        13.2.1   For a single output, connect the red circuit hoses to the system.

        13.2.2   For two separate outputs, connect both sets of hoses to the system.

    13.3   Set: System interconnection valve - open
                  Both tank selector valves - in
                  Both by-pass valves - open
                  Both flow control valves - closed
                  Pressure control valves - as previously preset (para. 11)

    13.4   Start the power unit (para. 15 or 16).

    13.5   Close both by-pass valves to load the system.

    13.6   On completing the bleeding operation, open both by-pass valves then stop the power unit.   Disconnect the hoses from the system.

BLEEDING THE HYDRAULIC SYSTEM

13.   After the trolley has been bled and preset (para 11) it may be used to bleed the hydraulic system as follows:-

    (1)   Ensure that the trolley return pressure valve has been correctly set, para 11 (10), and that the pressure control valves have been set to a suitable supply pressure, para 11 (9).

    Caution . . .

    If the hoses are connected to the hydraulic system before setting the return pressure valve, the contents of the system reservoir will be discharged into the trolley tank, which probably will overflow.

    (2)   Connect the hoses:-

        (a)   For a single output, connect the red circuit hoses to the system.

        (b)   For two separate outputs, connect both sets of hoses to the system.

    (3)   Set: System interconnection valve - open
                 Both tank selector valves - in
                 Both by-pass valves - open
                 Both flow control valves - closed
                 Pressure control valves - as preset (para 11)

    (4)   Start the power unit (para 15 or 16).

    (5)   Close both by-pass valves to load the system.

    (6)   On completing the bleeding operation, open both by-pass valves then stop the power unit. Disconnect the hoses from the system.

Fig. 10.1   Upper – operating instructions typed according to military specification.
Lower – same instructions typed with better type face and method of paragraph numbering.

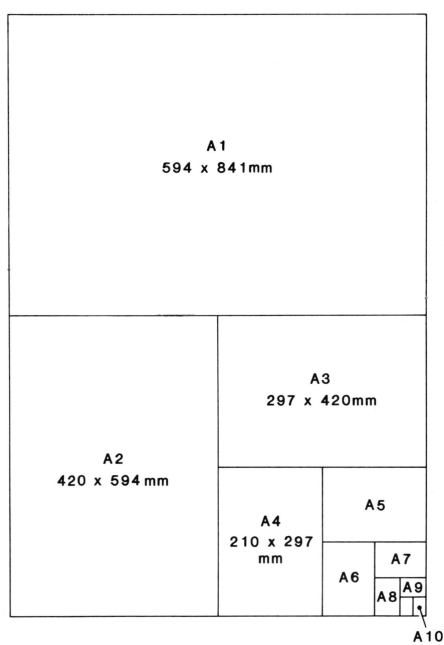

Fig. 10.2   An ISO A0 sheet divided into the 'A' series of sizes.

subject. The other specifications generally adopt a system of page numbering by chapters, so that each chapter begins with page 1. As a general rule, right-hand pages bear an uneven number, so that page 1 is a right-hand page.

Illustrations   Examples of illustration standards are given in each of the specifications, including such details as annotation sizes. The method recommended in ATA 100 for drawing electrical circuits differs from the left-to-right functional arrangement commonly used in Britain. There are considerable variations in the standards of the specimen illustrations, and examples that might be acceptable to one publication authority would almost certainly be rejected by another. Figure 10.3 right shows a simple cross-hatched orthographic section which some authorities would accept, while others would demand the more sophisticated shadow line and stippling techniques used on the left-hand section.

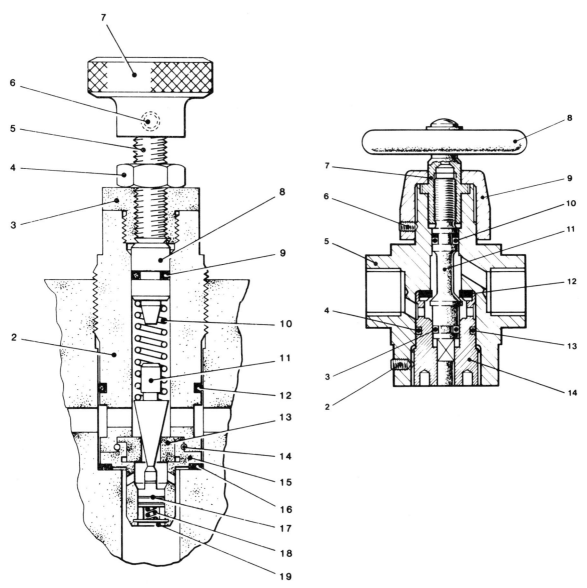

Fig. 10.3   Different standards for illustrations of orthographic sections.

Submission of synopsis and drafts   The procedure for preparing the synopsis and drafts and submitting these for approval is given in DG Ships 607B and CEGB TP 30. The other specifications do not define any procedures, although these could well be included in the contract authorizing the publication.

Arrangement of contents   In this area the philosophies of the four specifications vary enormously. At the one extreme we have DG Ships 607B which gives some general advice on the structure of publications for a ship, but for individual manuals relies on the first eight categories of BS 4884, as previously defined. Within these broad guidelines, the detailed contents for a particular publication are worked out by representatives of DG Ships and the publications contractor.

At the other extreme we have the enormously complicated publications structures specified in AvP 70 and ATA 100.

AvP 70 lists ten basic topics for equipment (excluding aircraft) into which the total information should be separated. Thus Topic 1 is General and Technical Information and Topic 4 is Planned Servicing Schedules.

When practicable, two or more topics can be combined within one publication. A further sixteen main topics are given for aircraft publications, and within these topics the information can be arranged in chapters as required. For equipment other than an actual aircraft, the required contents are specified in great detail. For an aircraft engine, for example, it is directed that the oil system must be covered in Chapter 7.

In ATA 100, the total information is segregated into groups of chapters, the identifying numbers of which are designated. Thus, the chapters covering a power plant are always numbered 70 to 91. Within such a group, each individual chapter broadly covers a particular system. Each chapter can be broken down into sections, and each section into subjects or units. The numbering system is pre-determined except for the last division which covers the subject or unit. Thus, Chapter 28 details the fuel system, Section 28–30 contains the distribution part of the fuel system and Section 28–40 embraces fuel contents indication.

CEGB TP 30 stipulates a relatively simple basic structure, in which the publications for a power station are divided into five volumes:

- Volume 1 – Design Concepts (prepared by the CEGB).
- Volume 2 – Plant Description.
- Volume 3 – Operating Instructions
- Volume 4 – Maintenance Instructions
- Volume 5 – Parts Lists

Each volume comprises as many books as may be necessary to accommodate the quantity of information. Within each volume, one chapter is normally allocated for each item of equipment. In Volume 2, the description of an exhaust spray cooling system would be allocated a separate chapter, and the operating instructions for this system would comprise a chapter in Volume 3.

HINTS FOR THE UNINITIATED

Publication specifications often seem to go to great lengths to state the obvious, yet fail to enlighten on the practical problems on which guidance is really needed. A hapless author may be faced with having to unravel a requirement enmeshed in a tangle of formal legalistic text, when all that is required is a simple example. As models of good technical communication, publication specifications sometimes leave much to be desired, and it is difficult to escape the conclusion that many specifications are compiled by people who, themselves, have never produced work to the standard that they demand of others. But that is not to say that all specifications are bad or useless. Many of their provisions, such as the use of standard page sizes and methods of presentation, are eminently sensible. And some of the requirements that may seem nonsensical in one context may be quite reasonable in another.

Many of us have heard a technical author say: 'I know this is a lot of nonsense, but I had to do it because that is what the specification requires.' I regard this attitude as unacceptable in a professional communicator. If adherence to the specification would result in something quite inappropriate, then contact the approving authority and argue it out with them. If your case is sound, they will usually agree to a liberal interpretation of the rules that will enable you to find a reasonable solution. Remember that you can have very good books and very poor books, all prepared in accordance with the same specification. The determining factors are the skill and application of the personnel concerned.

So, faced with the possibility of being entangled in a bureaucratic web of detailed specification requirements, what should the inexperienced communicator do? Fortunately, as so often happens in life, there are compensations. Most of the people in the approving authorities are quite reasonable common-sense folk, and if you can get to know them personally and discuss the project before you start work, few if any major problems will arise. Try to meet the person who will be responsible for examining and accepting your work.

The crux of the matter is to find out exactly what the requirements are, as seen through the eyes of the person who has to accept or reject the completed work. Within a given specification, there may be many possible interpretations, and the difference between one or other interpretation can mean a lot in terms of labour and cost.

Start by ensuring that your copy of the relevant specification is to the required revision standard, and make sure that you know the precise terms of the contract.

Read through the specification in the light of your knowledge of the equipment, and look for areas of uncertainty. Question phrases such as 'items listed in order of disassembly'. This may be obvious when dismantling a kitchen tap, but what is the order of disassembly for a car?

Find out the level of maintenance that will need to be covered and, in particular, whether overhaul instructions and spare parts information will be needed for all components. Enquire whether it is permissible to provide for bought-out items, such as a pump or electric motor, by including the literature provided by the component manufacturer in the form of an appendix. This is the sort of problem that can arise:

We had the task of compiling an illustrated parts catalogue for some equipment powered by a diesel engine of foreign manufacture. In a previous, similar situation, the customer had accepted the engine manufacturer's book as meeting the requirements for maintenance instructions. Would the manufacturer's parts catalogue, which was not up to the high standard required by the specification, be acceptable to the customer as meeting the parts catalogue requirement? If the manufacturer's catalogue were acceptable, we would be involved in virtually no work at all. On the other hand, if it were unacceptable, then we would become involved in redrawing all the detailed parts catalogue illustrations for the engine, researching all the part numbers and modification standards, and preparing a complete new engine parts catalogue. Almost certainly, it would have meant staff working abroad for a while at the manufacturer's factory, and the total cost would have been prodigious. It was arguable whether or not we could have claimed for any of the extra costs involved. Fortunately, after a period of uncertainty, the decision was eventually made in our favour and the existing catalogue was accepted.

Illustrations can be a very sensitive area with some publication authorities. Within the same authority, what may be quite acceptable to one of the illustration checking staff may be rejected by another. In these circumstances, too much reliance must not be placed on a literal interpretation of the specification. It is much more important that the person responsible for preparing the illustrations should meet the one responsible for checking them, and find out exactly what the requirements are. If this is done, a good working relationship can usually be established and there should be little trouble in the future.

The preparation of illustrated parts catalogues is another activity in which problems of interpretation can arise. When a component is produced by one company, included in the sub-assembly of another, which is installed in the main equipment produced by a third company and then given its own Ministry drawing number, what is its part number? Choose the wrong answer and, as a result, you may have to rewrite a part number index; this can be expensive. It is much better to ensure that you have all the correct answers to this type of question at the start of the project.

Having determined what you believe to be the requirements, submit typical samples and have these approved in writing before embarking on the bulk of the work. Then, if the publication authority subsequently demands a different standard, you will have a strong case for demanding payment for the additional work involved.

THE READER AS A SPECIFICATION WRITER

Finally, if among our readers there are those who, at some future date, may be required to prepare a publications specification, I implore them to learn from previous experience, and pay particular attention to the following five points.

First, the person in charge must be a very able writer who, himself, has written a variety of books on the type of equipment under consideration, and who has had practical experience of the problems of preparing such publications. A good illustrator must also be enlisted to advise on design, typography and the production of illustrations.

Second, avoid rigidity – treat the specification as a guide, rather than a set of mandatory rules. Inevitably, circumstances will arise which you have not foreseen, and the author must be given freedom of action to deal sensibly with such circumstances; rigid rules would preclude this.

Third, whenever possible, explain your requirements by giving actual examples. Contrast the following, which were taken from two British military specifications; the first almost defies comprehension; the second is quite simple.

Example 1 (awful)

21 The pages of the publication shall be numbered as follows:

21.1 Preliminary pages, in small roman numerals in parentheses and preceded by the word, 'page', e.g. 'page (i)' (Supp. 1 SS202 to SS207 series). The pages shall be numbered in one sequence throughout a single topic publication, but with different sequences for common pages and each set of separate topic pages in a multi-topic publication.

(*Author's Note:* Supp. 1 SS202 to SS207 refers to a set of style sheets contained in a supplementary volume.)

Example 2 (excellent)

This chapter gives typing instructions and is, itself, an example of the correct typing arrangement.

Fourth, when you have a draft of your specification, test it by having the next one or two books prepared in accordance with your draft. Alternatively, take some existing books and rewrite typical sections of them in accordance with your proposed specification.

Fifth, do not fall into the common trap of confusing optimum standardization that best facilitates the readers' understanding and access to information, with maximum standardization, that is standardization for its own sake. The former, when sensibly interpreted by competent illustrators and authors, can facilitate production of an efficient and coherent series of publications, but the latter is likely to result in manuals that are late, very expensive, with no creative flair and inferior to the books that would have been compiled if no specification at all had been invoked!

Sources of Information

LIST OF COMMON BRITISH STANDARDS

A technical communicator working in a specialized branch of technology or science will usually find that there is a British Standard or ISO Standard relevant to his work. For example, BS 4462 is a *Guide for the Preparation of Technical Sales Literature for Measuring Instruments and Process Control Equipment.*

There are also many more general standards which can apply to broad cross-sections of technological and scientific publications, of which the following are the most commonly used.

TITLE	BRITISH STANDARD NUMBER
Engineering Drawing Practice	BS 308
Conversion Factors and Tables	BS 350
Graphical Symbols for Telecommunications	BS 530
Symbols for use on Flow Diagrams of Chemical and Petroleum Plant	BS 974
Preparation and Correction of Mathematical Copy and Proofs	BS 1219
Manufacturers' Trade and Technical Literature (Sizes)	BS 1311
Page Sizes for Books	BS 1413
Glossary of Terms Used in Automatic Controlling and Regulating Systems	BS 1523
Graphic Symbols for General Engineering	BS 1553
Bibliographical References	BS 1629
Graphical Symbols and Abbreviations for Fire Protection Drawings	BS 1635

TITLE	BRITISH STANDARD NUMBER
Graphical Symbols for Process Measurement and Control Functions and Instrumentation	BS 1646
Sizes of Reprographic Papers	BS 1896
Letter Symbols, Signs and Abbreviations	BS 1991
Definitions for Use in Mechanical Engineering	BS 2517
Precise Conversion of Inch and Metric Sizes on Engineering Drawings	BS 2856
Graphical Symbols for Use in Diagrams for Hydraulic and Pneumatic Systems	BS 2917
Typeface Nomenclature & Classification	BS 2961
Glossary of Paper, Board, Pulp and Allied Terms	BS 3203
Graphical Symbols for Components of Servo-mechanisms	BS 3238
Schedule of Letter Symbols for Semi-conductor Devices and Integrated Circuits	BS 3363
Glossary of Terms Relating to Automatic Data Processing	BS 3527
Symbols for Machine Tools	BS 3641
Preparation of Indexes	BS 3700
International System (SI) Units	BS 3763
Glossary of Maintenance Terms in Terotechnology	BS 3811
Graphical Symbols for Electrical Power, Telecommunications and Electronics Diagrams	BS 3939
Sizes of Papers and Boards	BS 4000
Data Processing Flow Chart Symbols, Rules and Conventions	BS 4058
Lubrication Symbols	BS 4412
Glossary of Paper/Ink Terms for Letterpress Printing	BS 4149
Glossary of Terms used in Offset Lithographic Printing	BS 4277
Guide for the Preparation of Technical Sales Literature of Measuring Instruments and Process Control Equipment	BS 4462
Glossary of Electrotechnical, Power, Telecommunication, Electronics, Lighting and Colour Terms	BS 4727
Colour Proof Correction Symbols	BS 4785
Presentation of Technical Manuals	BS 4884
Copy Preparation and Proof Correction	BS 5261
Code of Practice for Documentation of Computer-Based Systems	BS 5515
British Standard Draft for Development containing advice on the presentation of tables, graphs and charts	DD 52

British Standards are obtainable from:

British Standards Institution, 101 Pentonville Road, London N1 9ND. Telephone 01-837 8801. Telex 23218.

EDUCATION AND TRAINING

Training in technical writing, technical illustration and technical publications techniques falls mainly within four broad categories:

The inclusion of limited tuition on writing and other aspects of information processing, as part of degree and diploma courses in engineering and science.

Short courses on report writing and other aspects of technical communication for managers, engineers and scientists. These are provided by commercial organizations specializing in this field as well as by some universities, polytechnics and colleges of further education. Sometimes courses are tailored to meet the needs of particular companies or organizations.

Training courses in technical authorship for people with previous engineering experience; these normally take the form of:

- Part-time courses at technical colleges.
- Full-time courses from six weeks to four months run by commercial organizations. These courses are usually sponsored by the Manpower Services Commission (MSC).
- Full-time courses from six to nine months run by technical colleges. These are usually sponsored by the MSC.
- Correspondence courses (a recent innovation).

Courses in technical illustration, full-time or part-time, at colleges of art and colleges of further education. Students normally enter these courses straight from school.

The City and Guilds of London Institute runs examinations in Technical Communication and Technical Authorship. Technical illustration courses are run under the auspices of DATEC (the Design and Art Committee of the Technical Education Council).

The ISTC Education and Training Committee keeps up-to-date information on training courses and examinations, and will be pleased to answer queries or provide further information; such requests should be addressed to:

The Secretary, Institute of Scientific and Technical Communicators, 17 Bluebridge Avenue, Brookmans Park, Hatfield, Herts AL9 7RY.

COPYRIGHT

Subject to certain exceptions, the copyright in an original literary work is vested automatically in the author. The same applies to artistic works (including drawings, diagrams, photographs and other illustrations), although if a photograph, portrait or engraving is commissioned and paid for, the copyright is vested in the person who commissioned it. The author of a literary or artistic work may either sell the entire copyright outright or, while retaining the copyright, license the use of the work in whole or in part either for publication in book or magazine form, or in other media, in accordance with agreed contractual arrangements.

The most important exception to the ownership provisions described above is that where an author or illustrator is an employee and produces the work 'in the course of his employment' then the copyright in the work is vested in the employer. Where articles are commissioned from freelance authors by newspapers or magazines, the author may be asked to assign the entire copyright to the magazine. Alternatively he may grant the publication no more than first British serial rights, normally defined as the right to publish in newspaper or magazine form for the first time within the UK and the Republic of Ireland, retaining all other rights.

The general conditions relating to copyright are set forth in the Copyright Act of 1956, which protects the author against unauthorized use of his material. There are, however, some exceptions: Part 1, Section 6 of the Act lists the general exceptions, including the following which are the most likely to apply to people engaged in scientific and technical publications.

6. General exceptions from protection of literary, dramatic and musical works.

(1) No fair dealing with a literary, dramatic or musical work for purposes of research or private study shall constitute an infringement of the copyright in the work.

(2) No fair dealing with a literary, dramatic or musical work shall constitute an infringement of the copyright in the work if it is for the purposes of criticism or review, whether of that work or of another work and is accompanied by a sufficient acknowledgement.

(3) No fair dealing with a literary, dramatic or musical work shall constitute an infringement of the copyright in the work if it is for the purpose of reporting current events –

(a) in a newspaper, magazine or similar periodical, or
(b) by means of broadcasting, or in a cinematograph film,

and in a case falling within paragraph (a) of this subsection, is accompanied by a sufficient acknowledgement.

(6) The copyright in a published literary or dramatic work is not infringed by the inclusion of a short passage therefrom in a collection intended for the use of schools, if –

(a) the collection is described in its title, and in any advertisements thereof issued by or on behalf of the publisher, as being so intended, and
(b) the work in question was not published for the use of schools, and
(c) the collection consists mainly of material in which no copyright subsists, and
(d) the inclusion of the passage is accompanied by a sufficient acknowledgement:

Provided that this subsection shall not apply in relation to the copyright in a work if, in addition to the passage in question, two or more other excerpts from works by the author thereof (being works in which copyright subsists at the time when the collection is published) are contained in that collection, or are contained in that collection taken together with every similar collection (if any) published by the same publisher within the period of five years immediately preceding the publication of that collection.

To facilitate the work of genuine scientific and other research workers and students, most leading publishers and learned societies subscribe to a

Fair Copying Declaration. This enables a student, critic, researcher or reviewer to make a single copy of part of a work, providing that it shall be used for his own non-profit-making purposes, that it shall not be sold or reproduced for publication, and that proper acknowledgement is made. Details of this Declaration are available in most large libraries.

Three useful 'Quick Guides' covering the more important practical details of copyright have been published by the Society of Authors. On payment of a small fee, these are available from:

The Society of Authors, 84 Drayton Gardens, London SW10 9SD.

ISTC BIBLIOGRAPHY ON TECHNICAL COMMUNICATION

Although first published in 1978, the ISTC Bibliography contains a wealth of references which are still valuable to anyone seeking further literature in the field of technical communication. The work was compiled in the Communication Studies Unit of the University of Wales Institute of Science and Technology by John Kirkman and Janis Peake. The Bibliography contains more than 1,300 references which are listed under the following headings:

- Scientific and Technical Writing (including business writing).
- Editing and Text Processing.
- Algorithms, Flow-charts, other Verbal-visual Techniques.
- Tables, Diagrams, Technical Illustration and Graphics.
- Typography, Printing, Production of Publications.
- Management, Planning and Control of Technical Publications.
- Oral Presentation of Technical Information.
- Meetings, Interviewing, Eliciting Information.
- Theoretical Background to Technical Communication.
- Standards and Symbols.
- Style – General: Grammar, Punctuation, Spelling, Usage.
- Technical Translation.
- Advice for Writers using English as a Foreign Language.
- Guides Issued by Professional Journals and Institutions.
- Indexing and Information Retrieval.
- Law.
- Bibliographies.

Copies of the Bibliography are available, on payment of a small fee from:

The Secretary, ISTC, 17 Bluebridge Avenue, Brookmans Park, Hatfield, Herts AL9 7RY.

The Institute of Scientific and Technical Communicators

17 Bluebridge Avenue, Brookmans Park,
Hatfield, Herts AL9 7RY

Objectives The ISTC is a professional body whose aim is to promote the highest standards among those involved in communicating technical information.

So often in industry technical problems are caused by an inadequate supply or total lack of information. If the personnel involved were given comprehensive, precise literature, many of the problems either might not arise at all, or could be quickly solved because the personnel would be properly equipped to deal with them. The provision of this information is the prime concern of the ISTC, and it can only be achieved by persons proficient in modern communication techniques and possessing a thorough understanding of the relevant branch of technology. Thus the ISTC draws its membership chiefly from industry, from the publications departments and agencies responsible for producing the bulk of the technical information necessary to an industrialized society.

History The ISTC was formed in 1972 by amalgamating three other similar bodies: the Presentation of Technical Information Group, formed in 1948; the Institute of Technical Authors and Illustrators (originally the Technical Publications Association), formed in 1953; and the Institute of Technical Publicity and Publications, formed in 1963.

Membership The ISTC's title was specifically chosen so as to encompass not only the technical authors and illustrators who form the majority of its membership, but also other specialists in technical communication, such as university lecturers in communication subjects; indeed anyone who shares similar interests and ideals in a field related to technical communication.

This is perhaps the greatest strength of the ISTC: that its membership embodies a great variety of specialist knowledge of the principles and practices involved in communicating scientific and technical information. Through its publications and meetings, the Institute plays a vital role in disseminating this knowledge throughout the growing profession.

Activities   In addition to its obvious role of striving to achieve the highest professional standards, bringing together practising communicators of all grades and disciplines, and providing a forum for debate and the exchange of professional information, the ISTC serves as the UK representative of INTECOM, the international body for technical communication. Institute members serve on the examining boards for City and Guilds technical publications examinations, and the Institute is represented on a number of policy-making bodies, such as the BSI (British Standards Institution).

The ISTC quarterly journal, *The Communicator of Scientific and Technical Information*, gives information on new ideas and techniques and provides a forum for discussion. *Communication News*, the monthly newsletter published between issues of the journal, keeps members informed of more mundane matters relevant to their profession. Virtually every scientific or technical innovation is likely to involve the technical communicator in some way or other.

Introduction to INTECOM

INTECOM – the International Council for Technical Communication – is an association of technical communication societies in various countries. Its main objectives can be summarized as follows:

- To improve the standards of writing, speaking and graphic communication in all applications of science and technology.
- To promote understanding of the importance of technical communication.
- To foster the formation of technical communication societies in countries where they do not yet exist.
- To facilitate the exchange of information and experience among member countries.
- To carry out projects of mutual interest to member countries.
- To assist member organizations in international matters.

How INTECOM was formed and how it is organized

INTECOM was constituted in 1970 by the communication societies in UK, the Netherlands, Sweden and the USA. INTECOM now represents or has established contacts in all countries where technical communication societies exist. The executive body of INTECOM is the Board of Officers which is elected among the Delegates of the General Assembly. The General Assembly is held every second year, and each member country is represented by two delegates nominated by the member organization(s) of the country. Between General Assemblies, the Board of Officers is responsible for the management of INTECOM. *Ad hoc* committees or working groups may be nominated for special projects.

This is INTECOM's area of interest

INTECOM has an area of interest which overlaps some other areas. This is illustrated in Figure A3.1. INTECOM aims at keeping in touch with developments in neighbouring areas and maintaining good contacts with organizations in those areas.

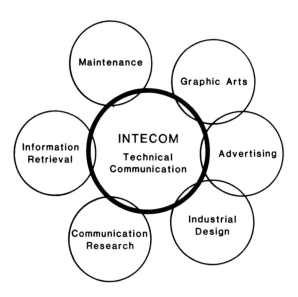

Fig. A3.1   Intecom – Spheres of operation.

What INTECOM can do

INTECOM is an organization through which international or national bodies can have direct access to expertise in technical communication. This can be used in many ways:

- INTECOM may give statements of opinion, from a technical communication viewpoint, on matters such as publication standards, education and training plans and syllabuses, codes of practice, professional standards, plans for communication research, etc.
- INTECOM may, through sub-committees, carry out projects of importance to other organizations and related to technical communication.
- INTECOM may serve as a contact point for organizations interested in technical communication.

Who are the people involved?

The individuals of INTECOM's member organizations are professional technical communicators. They work in industry, research associations, technical journals and publishing houses, consulting firms and in defence organizations. They may be writers, editors, managers, illustrators or educators. Together they constitute a professional group of extreme importance in our modern highly industrialized society. Their work is necessary if modern technology is to be utilized without danger to persons, great loss of time or excessive cost for running and maintaining equipment and systems. The communicators are in the front-line when modern technology is introduced to non-technical groups especially in developing countries. They represent a profession worthy of recognition and respect from other professional groups, governments and organizations.

Countries of member organizations include:

France	Norway
Germany	Sweden
Holland	United Kingdom
Israel	United States of America
Japan	

Index